BORES, BREAKERS, WAVES AND WAKES

FRONTISPIECE.—*The Mascaret on the Seine. Photographed on Sunday 16 September 1962 at 9.31 a.m. This Mascaret, though the highest associated with this series of spring tides, was by no means of exceptional height. It is here seen breaking over the quay at Caudebec, some 15 to 20 ft above the previous level of the river. (Photo by Miss Judith Tricker.)*

BORES, BREAKERS, WAVES AND WAKES

An Introduction to the Study of Waves on Water

R. A. R. TRICKER

M.A., Ph.D. (Cantab.), B.Sc. (Lond.)

MILLS & BOON LIMITED

50 Grafton Way, Fitzroy Square

London W1

First published 1964

© *R. A. R. Tricker 1964*

Made and Printed in Great Britain by Butler & Tanner Ltd, Frome and London

Contents

		PAGE
	PREFACE	xi
CHAPTER		
I	The Tides	1
	Appendix I	13
II	The Moon's Motion	15
III	The Tides as Observed	24
IV	Tidal Bores	33
V	An Elementary Theory of Tidal Bores	50
	Appendix II	64
	Appendix III	65
VI	The Theory of Gravity Waves in Shallow Water	67
	Appendix IV	79
VII	Waves as Seen from the Shore; the Properties of Waves in Shallow Water	81
VIII	Bernoulli's Theorem	101
IX	The Recording of Waves	112
X	Wave Spectra	121
XI	Waves in Deep Water	128
	Appendix V	135
XII	The Generation and Properties of Ocean Waves	138
XIII	Microseisms	148
XIV	Trochoidal Waves	155
XV	Eddies	169
	Appendix VI	184
XVI	Interference, Diffraction and Group Velocity	186
XVII	Ships' Wakes	201
XVIII	Surface Tension	215
XIX	Ripples	228
XX	Reflections in Rippled Water	240
	INDEX	247

v

List of Black and White Plates

PLATE		PAGE
1	The bore on the Mersey	40
2	The Aegir on the Trent	41
3	Usborne Moore's sketch of the bore on the Chien Tang Kiang	43
4	Bore shelter for Junks. Haining. (Sketch by Usborne Moore)	44
5	Simple wave tank	45
6	A bore travelling down the wave tank	47
7	Waves travelling down tubes of different diameters	48
8	Waves held stationary by an adverse current	51
9	A billiard ball rolling over a switchback in the form of a wave, to represent the motion of water particles in waves held stationary by an adverse current	72
10	Composite photograph of successive positions of the billiard ball	73
11	Wave of small amplitude in the wave tank	75
12	Wave of larger amplitude in the wave tank	75
13	Wave of large amplitude in the wave tank	76
14	Wave in a large tank in an experimental research station	76
15	Fall of pressure in a tube along which water flows	86
16	Pictures from a ciné film showing the reflection of waves from a breakwater	92
17	A reflected wave like that shown in the ciné film	93
18	Ripple tank photograph of the reflection of waves at a plane surface	93
19	Ripple tank photograph of the refraction of waves	95
20	Ping-pong ball held stationary in an air jet	103
21	The rotor ship *Buchau*	106
22	Eddy in the lee of a wave	144
23	Composite photograph to show the circular motion of water particles in wave motion	164
24	A photograph of the disc in the same positions as in the previous plate but with the wave moved on between each exposure	165

PLATE   PAGE

25 Streamline of flow past a stationary plate   169

26 The same streamlines photgraphed with the camera travelling
    with the water   170

27 The streamlines of the flow past a cylinder with the speed of
    the current of water very small   171

28 The streamlines with the speed of the water a little greater   172

29 The streamlines with a higher velocity of water   172

30 The flow past a cylinder and a streamlined body which has
    the same width at right angles to the flow   173

31 The eddies formed in the stream behind the cylinder, photo-
    graphed with the camera at rest relative to the water   173

32 and 33 Osborne Reynolds' experiment   175

34 Eddies in smoke rising from a cigarette   176

35 Smoke rings   179

36 Ripple tank photograph showing the passage of waves through
    an opening large compared with the wavelength   188

37 Ripple tank photograph of waves passing through an open-
    ing which is small compared with the wavelength   188

38 Addition of wave motions: first stage   190

39 Addition of wave motions: second stage   191

40 Addition of wave motions: third stage   191

41 Addition of wave motions: fourth stage   192

42 Addition of wave motions: fifth stage   193

43 Waves produced by a stone thrown into a pond   197

44 Group velocity   198

45 The wake generated by a swan   207

46 Aerial photograph of German mine-sweepers at work   208

47, 48, 49 and 50 Stages in the breaking away of a drop from the
    end of a tube   216

51 A rubber balloon filled with water   217

52 A needle floating on the surface of water   218

53 A large drop of engine oil floating in a mixture of alcohol and
    water   219

54 The alcohol–water mixture has been adjusted to have the
    same density as the oil and the shape of the drop then becomes
    spherical   219

PLATE   PAGE

55   Surface tension in a soap film   221

56   Surface tension in a soap film—second stage   221

57   Dissolved substances tending to decrease surface tension   224

58   Capillarity   225

59   Ripples in water. The stream is flowing just fast enough for
     the small object to cause ripples   234

60   Ripples just being formed by a 'fishing line' in very slowly
     running water   237

61   Ripples in water. The velocity of the stream increases   237

62   Ripples in water. As the velocity of the stream increases still
     further a wake, formed of two arms, starts to form   238

63   Ripples in water. Here the speed of the water is greater still   238

List of Colour Plates

Frontispiece: The Mascaret on the Seine

PLATE		FACING PAGE
II	The Severn Bore	2
III	The bore on the River Parrett	18
IV	The bore on the River Kent	18
V and VI	Stages of the passage of the Mascaret at Caudebec-en-Caux	35
VII	Spilling breakers	50
VIII	Spilling breakers	50
IX	A plunging breaker	67
X	The River Dee	82
XI	The formation of a wake by a light rowing boat	99
XII	The wake from a fast motor-boat in a river of limited depth	99
XIII	The wake from a steamer approaching Clifton Suspension Bridge	114
XIV	The formation of a wake by a fast motor-boat	114
XV	Reflection from the sun at low altitude	131
XVI	Reflections in a Scottish loch	146
XVII	Reflections in the river at Hereford	163
XVIII and XIX	Reflections in the Grand Canal, Venice	178
XX	Reflections of the sky	195

Preface

THE aim of this book is to bring an added interest and delight to times
spent by river, loch or sea. A study of waves on the surface of water has
not come within the reach of a large number of people and yet it is a
most attractive field of natural science. Apart from specialist works,
very few books of any sort have been written about it, so that it remains
an area in which the naturalist has been able to take only a very superficial interest. Yet an understanding of the processes which go on and
of their consequences can add very materially to the enjoyment to be
had from the contact all of us have from time to time with waves.

There can be few who have no interest at all in waves on water. We
have to make good the damage they do to our coasts and endure their
consequences whenever we travel by ship, but we can also enjoy their
magnificence and ever-changing patterns. To understand their mechanism can help to defeat the evil which they do and to increase the pleasure
of observation.

No doubt what has deterred very many from attempting a study of
waves on water has been the very formidable mathematics in which the
theory of the subject has been wrapped. It should be the function of
mathematics to render thinking easier and not to inhibit it. For the
expert mathematician this is, no doubt, always the case, but for those
who are not, mathematics has been more often an obstacle to be overcome rather than an aid to thought. For mathematics to serve its proper
purpose, therefore, it is necessary that it should be adjusted to the depth
of treatment which it is desired to give.

Most books on scientific subjects, other than those written for the
specialist, have aimed at eliminating the mathematics. For some, this is
perhaps desirable. Nevertheless, the results of mathematical reasoning
are often required for the development of the topics. The inevitable
outcome of such elimination of mathematical reasoning is that the results have to be quoted with little indication of their justification or
degree of credibility. The study becomes extremely superficial and un-
satisfying. Though possibly informative it leads to little understanding.
The reader is given no equipment with which he can extend his observations on his own account and he is left only with what he has been
told.

In this book a somewhat different objective has been set. Instead of
eliminating the mathematics, an attempt has been made to simplify it,
so as to bring it more within the compass of the general reader and
enable it to serve his thinking. It is hoped that in this way a better

appreciation of the subject will result. Such simplification of the mathematics has, of course, to be bought at a price. Inevitably there is some loss of rigour. Nevertheless, for many purposes the degree of approximation which can be achieved is often adequate, and a much better understanding of the basic physics is possible than would have been the case had the mathematical reasoning been eliminated entirely.

There are, of course, other dangers also. In bringing the mathematics within the reach of those equipped with only an ordinary level of attainment in the subject, the risk is run of boring those able to proceed faster. Such readers may indulge in judicious skipping. Then there is also the reader whose mathematics is more rudimentary than what has been assumed. The study of waves is one in which those interested are unlikely to be confined to those willing to work things out, even at the level at which this book is written. Those who experience difficulty with the mathematics may prefer to rely more directly on the results of experiment. Whenever possible, therefore, theoretical discussions have been provided with alternative approaches via experiment. As a rule these are of the simplest kind, requiring rudimentary apparatus, and are within the scope of everybody willing to take a little trouble to repeat them for himself. Thus, for example, the important relation

$$c = \sqrt{gD}$$

which gives the relation between the velocity of propagation, c, of waves in shallow water of depth D, upon which so many of the properties of waves depend, is arrived at on both theoretical and experimental grounds. All the apparatus required for the experiments is a long box rendered water-tight with a lining of plastic sheeting, which can be made by anyone in a very short time.

Ideally both theoretical and experimental approaches are desirable so that they may lend each other mutual support, but if it proves impossible to follow the theory, the experimental results furnish an alternative basis on which the topics can be studied.

It is not the purpose of this book to contribute to the subject by breaking new ground. Such originality as it possesses lies only in the methods of simplification employed. As Montaigne once said, 'I have gathered a nosegay of flowers in which there is nothing of my own except the string which ties them.' Even some of the methods of simplification have, no doubt, been found before. For example there is little doubt that the method employed for obtaining the pattern of ships' wakes must resemble that mentioned by Lord Kelvin but never published by him and now apparently lost. The simple method gives all the essential features of the calculations which Kelvin himself worked out with the aid of quite elaborate mathematics.

The author hopes that the enjoyment he has had in preparing the book will be obvious to the reader. Pictures can do small justice to the magnificence of many of the scenes with which the study brought him into contact. Of the photographs reproduced some he has taken himself. He is grateful to Miss Joan Dixon for the photograph of the bore on the River Kent and to Miss Mary Ennever and his daughter Judith for their help in photographing the Mascaret on the Seine from midstream at Caudebec-en-Caux. The latter also provided the originals for Plate XVII. The author has also to thank his sister, Mrs E. A. Holland, for the photographs for Plates XVIII and XIX, and he is deeply indebted to his wife for constant help in the production of the book.

Much help was provided with the utmost generosity by the National Institute of Oceanography, and particularly by its Principal, Dr G. E. R. Deacon, F.R.S., who very kindly went through the manuscript in detail. The author profited very greatly from his comments and advice.

He would also like to record his thanks to the Institute for permission to reproduce Figs. 87, 103, 104 and 105.

R. A. R. T.

Cropston

CHAPTER I

The Tides

MUCH of the fascination which a water surface has for most of us is due to the fact that it is rarely, if ever, still. Even the most stagnant of pools is disturbed from time to time by bubbles which rise from decaying vegetation and by insects which skate across its surface. The sea is for ever moving. A continually changing pattern is always presented.

Reflections from ripples and waves increase the difficulty of seeing into the body of the water, and things of which fleeting glimpses only can be obtained attract the attention, whether an interest in the fish and other inhabitants of the stream adds to it or not. These reflections are a conspicuous feature and provide a field of study in themselves.

Though large numbers of people devote much time and energy to the observation of nature, and water surfaces are a conspicuous feature of many natural situations which are met with on almost every country walk, not much close attention is often given to the waves and ripples with which they are marked. It is not so much to the fact that the properties of waves are not understood that this is due, as that the theory of the phenomena has hitherto been wrapped in very abstruse mathematics, beyond the reach of most people. Yet an understanding of the processes which are going on can add immensely to the enjoyment to be obtained from what is to be seen on almost every occasion, in town or country, when we venture into the open air. Very abstruse mathematics is not essential to a fairly extensive acquaintance with what is going on. The simplest principles of mechanics suffice to take us a considerable way, and the effort involved in mastering the application of broad general ideas is well worth the making. In this book we shall limit ourselves to what can be deduced by means of elementary considerations only, but at the same time these will open a wide field of interest to those who delight in the study of nature.

Waves on water range widely in their magnitude. From ripples, whose wavelengths are measured in millimetres, on the one hand, they extend to oscillations reaching over hundreds and even thousands of miles, on the other. In amplitude of oscillation, the range is a good deal less; amplitudes, measured by a fraction of a millimetre at the lower end, can attain a few tens of feet only at the upper. The fastest waves travel at hundreds of miles per hour whereas the slowest go at about only half a mile an hour.

The longest waves with which we have to deal are those of the tides.

Were it not for the complications introduced by the presence of land masses, the waves forming the tides would extend half-way round the world. Historically they were the first for which a theory was worked out and they still form a convenient starting point in the study of waves in general. In following this out we shall proceed, in fact, in order of decreasing wavelength, leaving the consideration of the shortest waves, or ripples, until the end. As we examine the properties of the tides when they enter rivers and estuaries, we shall find that they lead us to a theory of ordinary gravity waves in shallow water, which will enable us to discuss their most important properties.

The tides have, of course, an interest of their own, and they possess considerable importance for shipping, because of which they have received much attention. They display a variety of phenomena of great interest which have only been elucidated in the course of more than two centuries of study, though some are still unexplained. They are familiar to those who live near the shores of the great oceans and even to those on land-locked seas and lakes, though they are much less marked in these cases. They give rise to currents which have cost many lives as well as helped or hindered ships on their way, and they have attracted the attention of those interested in the happenings of nature from the earliest times. We will start off, therefore, with an elementary account of how the tides are formed and discuss some of their principal characteristics.

The timing of the tides has obvious connections with the movement of the moon, but it was not until the time of Newton that the connection began to be understood. Galileo, for example, upbraids Kepler for having 'given his ear and consent to the Moon's predominancy over the Water, and to occult properties and suchlike trifles'.[1]

Newton's contribution was both direct and indirect. Indirectly through his theory of universal gravitation he laid the basis for a possible explanation of the action of the sun and the moon on the waters of the earth. He did more than this, however. He contributed directly through his investigation into what is now called the 'Equilibrium Tide'—that is, he investigated the tide-raising forces. His theory, which is given in Book 1, Proposition 66, of the *Principia*, is basically correct, though he emphasized the importance of the vertical component of the tide-raising force, whereas it has since become apparent that it is the horizontal component which is the important one. He was not unaware of the dynamical aspects either and explained how the inertia of the oceans would modify the action of the tide-raising forces. His theory of the tides was continued in Book III, Proposition 24. Here he gives the

[1] From Galileo's *System of the World* quoted via Memorial Volume to Isaac Newton prepared for the Mathematical Association.

PLATE II.—*The Severn Bore.*

correct theory of spring and neap tides, the variation in spring tides which are highest when the moon is at perigee, 'priming and lagging', the higher tides of the northern winter compared with the summer, the effects of the declination of the sun and the moon and the resulting highest springs at the equinoxes.

These points will be discussed later, but here it is interesting to note how far Newton was able to carry his initial investigations, a burden he supported almost entirely on his own shoulders. He compared the results of his theory with what was then known of the tides in various parts of the world. A case of special interest was his account of the tide at the 'port of Batsham in the Kingdom of Tonquin in the latitude of 20° 50' north' (the latitude corresponds to Hanoi): 'There are two inlets to this port and the neighbouring channels,' he said, 'one from the seas of China between the continent and the island of Luconia, and the other from the Indian sea, between the continent and the island of Borneo.' Newton had already explained how two tides arriving by different channels would produce one high and one low water and not double high water, or double low water, or both, as might, perhaps, at first sight have been supposed. Professor Proudman[1] said: 'It is impossible not to contrast the soundness of this remarkable paragraph with the absurdity of the popular explanation of the double high water at Southampton, more than two centuries later.'

In this chapter we will consider a simple development of the theory of the equilibrium tide. In doing this we shall be able to include most of the problems considered by Newton. Though we shall thus reach much the same position as he attained, the methods will not be quite the same as he employed. Many books state the fact that the tide-raising forces generated by the moon are such as to tend to produce a heaping up of the seas at the point where the moon is overhead and also on the opposite side of the earth, but few give a simple explanation of how this can occur. At first sight the occurrence of a second high water on the side of the earth facing away from the moon appears paradoxical, the general statement that on the far side the moon pulls the earth away from the oceans, which is sometimes made, being very unconvincing. Yet how the second high water occurs is not difficult to understand.

Because of the mutual attraction of the earth and the moon the two bodies revolve about their common centre of gravity. The gravitational force which each exerts upon the other provides the force which is required to make them each describe its orbit about this point. To make a mass describe a circle it is necessary to act upon it with a force which is directed to the centre of the circle. This is the case, for example, if a body is whirled round on the end of a string. The tension in the string

[1] Contribution to Memorial Volume to Isaac Newton already quoted.

B

pulls the body inwards and prevents it from flying off at a tangent. This
force which has to be applied to cause the body to travel in a circle is
known as the centripetal force. If, as a first approximation, it is assumed
that the earth describes a circular orbit of radius r about the common
centre of gravity with velocity v, then the gravitational attraction of the
moon must provide the centripetal force. The actual value of the centripetal force in this case is $\dfrac{Ev^2}{r}$, E being the mass of the earth. We do not,
however, require to know its precise value. It will suffice if we denote
by F the force required to cause a particle of mass m to move in a circle
of radius r at a speed v.

It is necessary at the outset to get clear on two points. The first is that
the earth-moon system does not revolve about the common centre of
gravity, as a rigid body. If the earth were connected to the moon by a
rigid bar it would always present the same face to the moon and this it
does not do. However, even if it did always present the same face to the

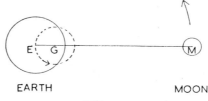

EARTH   MOON

FIG. I.

moon, there would still be no constraint, apart from the very slow action
of the friction of the tides, to make it do so, and in considering a
phenomenon having a principal period of 12 hours, forces which can
produce an effect only in a time which is long even on a geological scale
can be neglected. The second point is that the rotation which the earth
does, in fact, possess about its axis is similarly not related to the gravitational action of the moon over limited periods of time, and can be considered separately. We will, therefore, first consider the action of the
moon on an earth which is not rotating relative to the stars, as it describes its circular orbit about the common centre of gravity of the earth
and the moon.

The common centre of gravity of the earth and the moon lies, in fact,
within the earth, about three-quarters of its radius distant from the
centre. This may be somewhat confusing but where the point about
which the earth revolves is situated actually makes no difference at all.

As the moon revolves about G, the common centre of gravity of the
earth and the moon, in an anticlockwise direction as viewed from the

pole star, the centre E of the earth describes a circle in the same direction about the same point, as in Fig. 1. Let the radius of this circle be r.

If the earth does not rotate on its axis as its centre revolves about G, then any point, P, on its surface (or within its volume) will also describe a circle with the same radius r but about a point G' such that PG' is equal and parallel to EG. To convince oneself of the truth of this, take a piece of card and push two pencils through it at two points corresponding to E and P. Then, always keeping EP parallel to its original

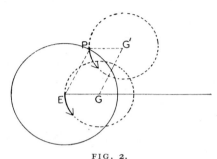

FIG. 2.

direction, so that the card is not allowed to rotate, trace out any curve with the pencil E on a piece of paper. The pencil P will obviously trace out an identical curve displaced a distance equal to EP in the direction of this line.

If now we consider a particle of mass m placed at P, it is clear that to make it describe its circle of radius $PG' = EG = r$, it must be acted on by a force F. Every particle of which the earth is composed will describe a circle of the same radius r and each must, therefore, be provided with a force F directed towards the centre of its circle, to enable it to do so.

EARTH   MOON

FIG. 3.

The line joining P to the centre of its circle is parallel to the line joining the centre of the earth to the centre of the moon. The direction of this force F is, therefore, the same for all particles.

Fig. 3 is a diagram of the earth-moon system drawn approximately to scale. Although the distance of the moon from the earth is large (about 240,000 miles) it is not so large that lines drawn from the moon's centre to various points on the earth's surface are not inclined appreciably to the line to the centre of the earth, and there is also an appreciable

variation in their length. Thus the diameter of the earth subtends an
angle of 2° at the moon and the point on the earth opposite the moon is
3 per cent nearer to it than the point on the other side of the earth. It
is to these variations in distance and direction that the tide-raising forces
produced by the moon on the earth's surface are due.

To see how this comes about consider Fig. 4, which is based on
Fig. 3 but distorted somewhat to bring out these variations in distance
and direction of the moon's centre, as seen from various points on the
earth's surface.

The radius r of the orbit which the earth describes about G will be
determined by the average force of attraction exerted by the moon on all
the particles in the earth. It corresponds to the orbit which would be
described by a particle placed at the centre of the earth under the
action of the moon's attraction alone.

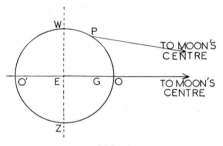

FIG. 4.

Newton's Law of Gravitation is that every particle attracts every
other particle in the universe with a force which is proportional to the
product of their masses and inversely proportional to the square of the
distance between them. If the two masses are M_1 and M_2 and R is their
distance apart, the gravitational force may be written as

$$G\frac{M_1 . M_2}{R^2}$$

In this expression G is a constant, known as the constant of gravitation. Thus, if D is the distance between the centre of the earth and
that of the moon, the force a particle of mass m at the centre of the earth
experiences will be $G\dfrac{Mm}{D^2}$, where M is the mass of the moon and G the
constant of gravitation. This force must equal F.

Now a particle of mass m placed at P will be attracted by the moon
with a force which is greater than F when P is to the right of WZ and
less than F when it is to the left, since it is nearer to the moon in the

first case and farther away in the second. Let us call the force of attraction which the moon exerts on the particle L. The force will also be inclined to the direction of EG except when P lies on this line at O or O'. But for the particle at P to describe its circle of radius r requires a force F in a direction parallel to EG. The moon's attraction provides the force L which is neither of quite the correct magnitude nor quite in the required direction to cause the particle to describe the circular path which it does.

Were the earth a rigid body the difference between the attraction exerted by the moon and the force F required to cause the particle to move in its circular orbit, would be provided by internal forces in the earth. When the earth is fluid, however, these internal forces cannot produce this difference and what is left outstanding gives rise to the tide-producing forces.

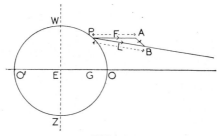

FIG. 5.

Referring to Fig. 5, let us draw PA to represent F parallel to EG. It will therefore represent the centripetal force required to make the particle P move in its circle. It will always have to be of the same length wherever P is placed on the earth's surface. When P is in the position indicated in Fig. 5, the force exerted on the particle by the moon's attraction will be greater than PA and will be directed towards the centre of the moon. Let us represent the force of the moon's attraction by PB. The force PB is seen to be equivalent to two forces PA and AB, by the triangle of forces. The force PA causes the particle to describe its circular orbit; the force AB is the force which is left over. This would be counteracted were the earth rigid but it forms the tide-raising force on an earth covered by oceans.

When the particle P is placed at the point such that PE is at right angles to EG, as in Fig. 6, the force of attraction of the moon is approximately equal to the force it exerts upon a similar particle at the centre of the earth; that is to say it is approximately equal to F. Thus PA and PB are of the same length but inclined at a small angle to each other. The tide-raising force AB is, therefore, directed vertically downwards.

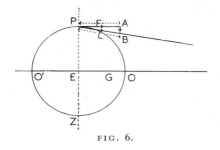

FIG. 6.

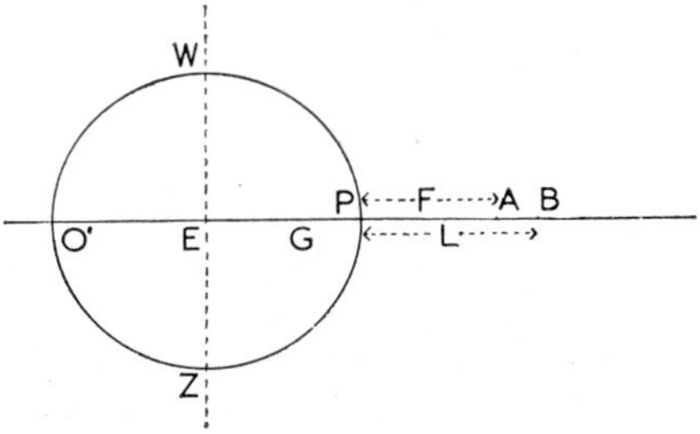

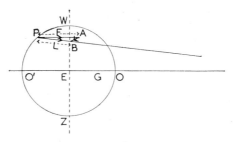

FIG. 7.

When the particle P is vertically under the moon, as in Fig. 7, the moon's attraction is greater than on a particle at the earth's centre, but PA and PB are now both in the same direction. The tide-raising force, AB, is thus directed vertically upwards.

FIG. 8.

When the particle P is placed to the left of the line WZ, as in Fig. 8, it is farther from the moon than it would be if placed at the centre of the earth and the attractive force of the moon upon it is less than F.

PB is now less than *PA* so that the tide-raising force *AB* is directed as indicated in Fig. 8.

When the particle is placed at *O′* on the opposite end of the diameter to *O*, as in Fig. 9, *PB* is still less than *PA* although it again possesses the same direction. The tide-raising force is again vertical but this time it is directed away from the moon and not towards it.

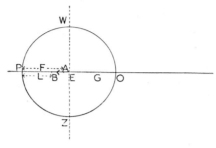

FIG. 9.

Fig. 10 is drawn to summarize this discussion and shows the direction of the tide-raising forces over the surface of the earth.

There remains one point to discuss and this is that the vertical component of the tide-raising force is simply added to or subtracted from the weight of the particle. It is very small compared to the force of

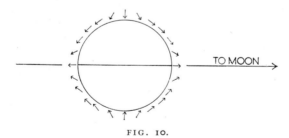

FIG. 10.

gravity at the earth's surface and is of little importance. It is the horizontal component which is effective in producing the tides. The horizontal component is indicated in Fig. 11, the lengths of the arrows indicating the magnitude of the force.

The horizontal forces may be thought of as giving rise to the equilibrium tide, and they are in such directions as to cause two high waters, one directly under the moon and the other on the opposite side of the earth.

As the earth rotates, points on its surface are carried round and pass twice a day under places where conditions favour high water and twice under places where they favour low water. The simple theory of the equilibrium tide is thus capable of explaining what is probably the most conspicuous feature of the tides, namely that they occur approximately twice a day. They are, however, tied to the apparent motion of the moon

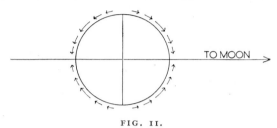

FIG. 11.

rather than the sun so that, because of the movement of the moon in its orbit, the time between successive high waters is rather longer than 12 hours. All this is in accord with observation.

The equilibrium tide, however, is a purely conceptual affair and has little other correspondence to the tides of reality. It neglects the dynamical aspects of the problem entirely. The waters of the oceans

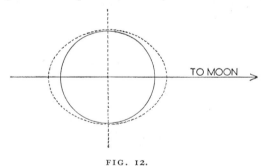

FIG. 12.

possess inertia and would not take up a position of equilibrium instantaneously under the action of the tide-raising forces, even if complications introduced by the existence of land masses on the earth's surface did not occur. Nevertheless, the concept of an equilibrium tide is by no means valueless. It must be looked upon, however, solely as a summary in a convenient form of the disposition of the tide-raising forces.

It is of some importance to know how the tide-raising forces vary with the distance of the body which gives rise to them. It is fairly easy to see, in the two extreme cases of points on the earth directly under the moon and of points removed 90° from this position, that the tide-raising force will vary inversely as the cube of the distance of the object which produces them. Consider first the case where the point is directly opposite the moon on the earth's surface. Here the centripetal force F and the force caused by the moon's attraction are in the same straight

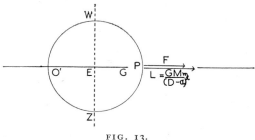

FIG. 13.

line. If a is the radius of the earth, the force of the moon's attraction on a particle at this point will be $\dfrac{G.M.m}{(D-a)^2}$. The tidal force is the difference between the moon's attraction and the centripetal force. Expanding the expression for the moon's attractive force to the first order in $\dfrac{a}{D}$ we have

$$\frac{G.M.m}{(D-a)^2} = \frac{G.M.m}{D^2} + \frac{2a.G.M.m}{D^3}$$

[Those unfamiliar with this binomial expansion can understand it if we assume that a is a small fraction, say x per cent, of D. $D-a$ will thus be less than D by x per cent and $(D-a)^2$ will be less than D^2 by $2x$ per cent. The fraction $\dfrac{1}{(D-a)^2}$ will therefore be increased by $2x$ per cent, that is by $\dfrac{2a}{D}$ of its value.

Thus when D is changed to $D-a$, the expression $\dfrac{G.M.m}{D^2}$ will increase by a fraction $\dfrac{2a}{D}$ of its value—that is by

$$\frac{2a}{D} \cdot \frac{G.M.m}{D^2} = \frac{2aG.M.m}{D^3}\Bigg]$$

Thus, the first term on the right-hand side being the force which the moon would exert on the particle if placed at the centre of the earth and therefore equal to F, the difference between the force which the moon actually exerts on the particle and F, which is the tidal force, is

$$\frac{G.M.m}{(D-a)^2} - F = \frac{2a.G.M.m}{D^3}$$

The force, in this case in the vertical direction, thus varies inversely as the cube of the moon's distance.

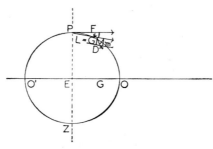

FIG. 14.

When P is in the direction at right angles, as in Fig. 14, the centripetal force and the force of the moon's attraction, $\dfrac{G.M.m}{D^2}$, will be equal in magnitude but inclined at a small angle to each other. The resultant force, AB (again vertical), will be given by the product of one of the forces and ε, the angle between them.

Thus the resultant force will be

$$\frac{G.M.m}{D^2}\varepsilon$$

To a first approximation $\varepsilon = \dfrac{a}{D}$ and thus the resultant force becomes

$$\frac{G.M.m}{D^3}a$$

Again it varies inversely as the cube of the moon's distance.

This result is generally true whatever the position of P may be on the surface of the earth. The calculation in the general case is not difficult, but to avoid unnecessarily cumbering up the text it has been given in Appendix I.

That the tide-raising forces vary inversely as the cube of the distance of the object producing them is important. It shows, for example, that changes in the distance of the object have large effects. A change of

1 per cent in the moon's distance will lead to a change of 3 per cent in its tide-raising properties. The moon's distance varies between 222,000 miles and 253,000 miles. Its mean distance is about 240,000. The nearest distance of approach is thus 7·5 per cent less than the mean. The effectiveness of the moon in raising tides may therefore be expected to increase by some 22 per cent of the mean as it moves into its position of closest approach to the earth (perigee) and to decrease by about 16 per cent as it moves into its farthest position (apogee).

The sun will generate tides in precisely the same manner as the moon. The sun is about 27,100,000 times more massive than the moon but it is about 389 times more distant. The tide-raising forces produced by the sun would therefore be expected to be $\dfrac{27,100,000}{389^3}$ times, that is 0·460 times, those of the moon. Thus the great mass of the sun compared with that of the moon is more than compensated by its greater distance.

APPENDIX I

To show that the tide-raising force varies inversely as the cube of the distance of the object giving rise to it

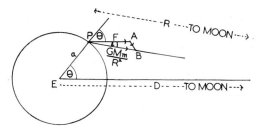

FIG. 15.

Consider a particle of mass m at P (Fig. 15).

It is acted on by an attraction due to the moon of $\dfrac{G.M.m}{R^2}$, where R is the distance from P to the moon.

Approximately $R = D - a \cos \theta$.

The centripetal force necessary to cause P to describe its circular orbit is F and as before this is equal to $\dfrac{G.M.m}{D^2}$.

The tide-raising force is equal to the resultant of the two forces PB and AP.

We are interested only in the horizontal component. Therefore resolving along the direction of the tangent at P we have:

The horizontal component of PA is

$$PA \sin \theta = F \sin \theta = \frac{G.M.m}{D^2} \sin \theta$$

The horizontal component of BP is $\dfrac{G.M.m}{R^2} \sin (\theta + \varepsilon)$

Therefore the horizonal component of their resultant will be the difference between these; that is to

$$\frac{G.M.m}{R^2} \sin (\theta + \varepsilon) - \frac{G.M.m}{D^2} \sin \theta$$

$$= \frac{G.M.m}{(D - a \cos \theta)^2} \sin (\theta + \varepsilon) - \frac{G.M.m}{D^2} \sin \theta$$

$$= \frac{G.M.m}{D^2} \left(\sin (\theta + \varepsilon) + \frac{2a}{D} \cos \theta \sin (\theta + \varepsilon) - \sin \theta \right)$$

to the first order in $\dfrac{a}{D}$.

The angle $\varepsilon = \dfrac{a \sin \theta}{D}$ and is very small, and to the first order, $\sin \varepsilon = \varepsilon$ and $\cos \varepsilon = 1$. Also $\varepsilon . a/D$ is of the second order of small quantities and may be neglected in a first approximation.

Substituting these values, the expression for the horizontal component of the tide-raising force becomes

$$\frac{G.M.m}{D^2} \left(\sin \theta + \cos \theta . \varepsilon + \frac{2a}{D} \cos \theta \sin \theta - \sin \theta \right)$$

$$= \frac{G.M.m}{D^2} \left(\frac{a}{D} \sin \theta \cos \theta + \frac{2a}{D} \sin \theta \cos \theta \right)$$

$$= \frac{3a}{2} \frac{G.M.m}{D^3} \sin 2\theta$$

This formula is in agreement with the qualitative account given in Chapter I. The horizontal component of the tide-raising force varies as $\sin 2\theta$. It is therefore zero in the direction immediately underneath the moon and also in the direction at right angles to this. It has its maximum value half-way between. It also varies inversely as the cube of the distance D.

CHAPTER II

The Moon's Motion

WE have already considered the effect on its tide-raising powers of variations in the distance of the moon from the earth. The most obvious cause of variation in the tides, however, is the relation between those raised by the sun and those raised by the moon. This gives rise to the phenomenon of spring and neap tides. At times of new and full moon the equilibrium tides of the sun and moon coincide in position and their tide-raising forces reinforce each other. We then have spring tides of greatest amplitude. Spring tides thus recur at approximately fortnightly intervals. The highest tides, however, take some time to build up and occur one or two days after new or full moon. This lag is known as the 'Age of the Tide'. It varies from $1\frac{1}{2}$ days in the North Atlantic to several days elsewhere. It used to be explained as the time required for the tide, which was thought to be generated in the waters of the southern ocean, which are unimpeded by land masses, to reach the other parts of the world, but this explanation is no longer supported. A satisfactory explanation of the age of the tides has yet to be found. The interval between springs and new moon is approximately the same as that between neaps and quadrature. When the moon is in its quarters its equilibrium tide is out of phase with that of the sun. The moon's high water coincides with the sun's low water and vice versa. At these periods the tidal range is least and the tides are then known as neaps. Since the tide-raising forces produced by the sun are only 0·46 of those of the moon, the ratio of the equilibrium spring tides to the neaps is $\frac{1·46}{0·54}$, which is about $\frac{8}{3}$.

Since the effectiveness of the moon is greatest at perigee, the highest spring tides are formed when perigee falls at either new or full moon. These are the so-called perigee springs. Were the moon's orbit an ellipse fixed in space, perigee springs would be expected to occur on two fixed occasions in the year, once when new moon coincided with perigee and once when full moon occurred at this time. Because of the rotation of the axes of the moon's orbit this does not occur. Perigee also does not fall back evenly around the lunar month but remains close to new moon for about three months. It then shifts rapidly through the quarters, again steadying up or 'hanging' near full moon. The consequent perigee springs with the maximum lunar effect recur for about three months in succession during the year.

The distance of the sun from the earth also varies. We are nearer to the sun in the winter than in the summer. When the earth in its orbit round the sun is at its point of closest approach it is said to be in perihelion (the sun is then said to be in perigee). The tide-raising forces produced by the sun will therefore have their greatest magnitude at this time. Tides, therefore, tend to be greater in winter than in summer. The effect caused by the variation in distance of the sun is much less than the corresponding effect of the moon. At its closest approach in early January, the sun is only 1·7 per cent nearer than the average. Its tide-raising forces are therefore only about 5 per cent greater. Similarly in early July when the sun is at its farthest from the earth its tide-raising forces will be 5 per cent smaller.

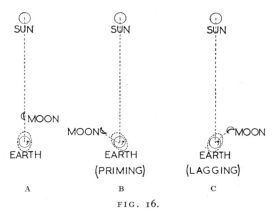

FIG. 16.

When two simple harmonic motions of the same period are combined they result in another simple harmonic motion of the same period as before but with a different amplitude and displaced in time. They do not give rise to double peaks. The main components of the tides raised by both sun and moon are approximately semi-diurnal and thus possess nearly the same period (12 hours and 12 hours 25 minutes respectively). They will combine therefore to give a resultant semi-diurnal tide with successive high waters at intervals of about 12 hours. The resultant equilibrium tide occupies an intermediate position between those of the sun and the moon. The effect is to put the tides somewhat out of step with the moon. It is known as 'priming' and 'lagging' of the tide. At new (and full moon) as in Fig. 16 A high water of the equilibrium tide occurs as the moon culminates. During the first quarter, as in Fig. 16 B, high water of the equilibrium tide occurs before the moon crosses the meridian. This is known as 'priming'. In the last quarter high water of the equilibrium tide occurs after the moon has crossed the meridian, which is known as 'lagging'.

The plane of the orbit of the earth is inclined at an angle of $23\frac{1}{2}°$ to the equator. The plane of the moon's orbit is inclined to that of the earth by 5° 9'. The two planes intersect in a line which rotates round the earth's orbit in a period of 18·6 years. The moon's orbit may therefore be inclined by as much as $28\frac{1}{2}°$ to the equator, this maximum inclination occurring once in 18·6 years. The angular distance of an object above or below the equator is known as its declination. The declination of the moon has very important bearings on the tides.

Consider the equilibrium tide when the moon has some positive declination δ. The line joining the two points of high water will be in the direction of the moon and will be inclined to the plane of the equator (see Fig. 17.). A point P on the earth's surface will be carried round the

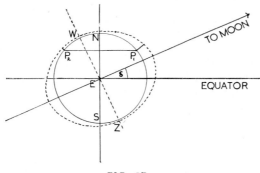

FIG. 17.

small circle P_1P_2 as the earth rotates. At P_1, when it is opposite the moon, it will experience a high tide and again when it arrives at P_2. The high tide at P_1 will, however, be higher than the high tide at P_2. The effect of declination, therefore, is to introduce an inequality into the tides. High tides will be alternately large and small. The main constituent of the tides has a period of about 12 hours and is known as a semi-diurnal tide. The period of the inequality introduced by the declination of the moon is diurnal. The actual tide will be the resultant of a semi-diurnal and a diurnal tide. The effect of this is illustrated in Fig. 18. The dotted curve represents a simple harmonic semi-diurnal tide. The dashed curve is the diurnal tide and the full line is the resultant. The high tides H_1, H_2, H_3, . . . are seen to be alternately greater and smaller. The declination of the sun will introduce a similar effect with regard to the solar tides.

Newton pointed out another possible effect of declination. If the

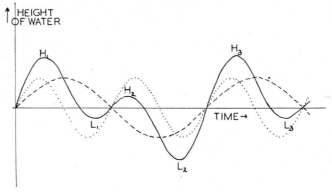

FIG. 18.

moon were over the north pole, he said, there would be no variation in
the level of the sea as the earth rotated. The sea would simply be displaced permanently towards the poles. From this he concluded that
declination tends to reduce the tidal range and hence he expected that
the greatest tides would occur at the equinoxes when the declination of
the sun becomes zero, especially if the declination of the moon was also
small at the time.

It is possible for one high water to be suppressed altogether and the
resultant tide becomes entirely diurnal, as in Fig. 19.

The greatest declinational effect will be obtained when both sun and
moon have their greatest declinations together, that is when the moon's
greatest positive declination occurs at the summer solstice or its greatest

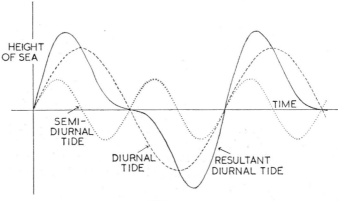

FIG. 19.

PLATE III.—*The bore on the River Parrett.*

PLATE IV.—*The bore on the River Kent. (Photo by Miss J. H. Dixon.)*

negative declination at the winter solstice. Declination also introduces an inequality into the timing of high and low water. Thus the time from high water to low water is not the same as the time from low water to high water.

The motion of the moon introduces a number of other periodicities into the tides. The lunar month is determined by the time between successive conjunctions of the moon and the sun. The earth, however, describes an appreciable arc of its orbit round the sun in a lunar month (about 29°) so that the lunar month is not the period of the moon in its orbit. The position can be understood from Fig. 20.

The period of the moon's revolution in its orbit is $27\frac{1}{4}$ days, but since the sun has moved on in this time the moon does not again come into conjunction with the sun until another $2\frac{1}{4}$ days have elapsed. The length

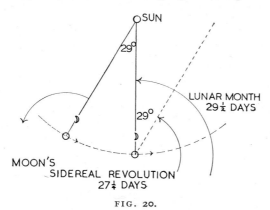

FIG. 20.

of the lunar month (from new moon to new moon) is, therefore, about $29\frac{1}{2}$ days. To simplify the figure the movement of the earth in the interval of $2\frac{1}{4}$ days between the completion of the moon's motion in its orbit and the time it again comes into conjunction with the sun, has not been indicated in Fig. 20.

The axis of the moon's orbit rotates and thus the intervals from perigee to perigee are not the same as the period of revolution of the moon in its orbit. The journey from perigee to perigee takes $27\frac{1}{2}$ days.

There are also a number of slower periodic components in the moon's motion, which also affect the tides. Thus the axis of the moon's orbit rotates once in 8·8 years. The nodes of the moon's motion (the points in which the moon crosses the plane of the earth's orbit) revolve in 18·61 years. The coincidence of the line of centres of the earth, moon and sun recurs after 18·03 years, a cycle known as the cycle of Saros. It has been

c

used since ancient times in the forecasting of eclipses. There is also the
Metonic cycle of 19 years, which is a period after which the moon's
phases recur. It is not possible to utilize any of these cycles for the
purpose of avoiding a fresh prediction of the tides, since in none of
them do all the factors return to their initial values.

The movement of the sun similarly gives rise to another series of
cycles. It will not be necessary for the purposes of this book to go into
the details of the calculations, but the tides are predicted by finding for
a given place where the tides have to be determined, the amplitudes and
phases of a number of harmonic constituents. This harmonic analysis
of tidal observations is a very laborious process even though the periods
to be looked for are given from considerations of the equilibrium tide.
Once the amplitude and phases of the constituents have been obtained
the height of the sea at any time can be obtained by calculating the

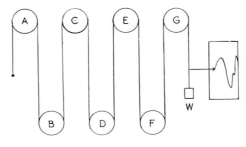

FIG. 21.

values of each constituent at that time and adding the results. If only
the time of high and low water is required this process may be feasible,
but the number of components required for accurate prediction is quite
large and to compute the height of the sea for each hour of the day
throughout the year becomes very laborious, using ordinary methods
of computation. The amplitudes and phases of each of the constituents
having been obtained, however, the values for any time can be added
mechanically.

The idea of constructing a tide-predicting machine was first put
forward by Lord Kelvin. The principle he employed in summing the
constituent simple harmonic motions is illustrated in Fig. 21.

A single wire passes round the pulleys A, B, C, D, . . . and is kept
stretched by a weight W. This end of the wire also carries a pen which
records on a rotating drum. Each of the pulleys is moved up and down
in a simple harmonic motion corresponding to one of the tidal constituents. It is arranged that positive values of the constituents corre-

spond to movements of the pulleys *A, C, E, G,* . . . upwards or to
movements of the pulleys *B, D, F,* . . . downwards. The wire thus adds
all the constituents together for any time and moves the pen accordingly.
Each pulley is given its vertical harmonic motion by means of the crank
and slot illustrated diagrammatically in Fig. 22. The crank pin *P* is
attached to the arm *PO* which is rotated by gear wheels at the appropriate rate so as to correspond to one of the tidal constituents. The
length of the arm *PO* is adjusted to correspond to the amplitude of the
constituent. The crank slides in the slot in the horizontal bar which
itself can move in guides in a vertical direction. The pulley is pivoted
to the bar and thus moves up and down with the required simple
harmonic motion.

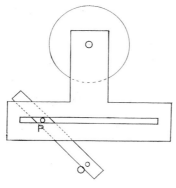

FIG. 22.

The construction of the machine is by no means easy since the gearing
of the cranks to give the correct period is not simple. Machines are in
use, however, capable of giving accurate predictions for a year at a time.
In use, the settings are checked periodically while the forecast is being
made. The height of the sea is, in fact, indicated on a dial rather than
on a graphical record as this is found to be more accurate and the data so
obtained are ready for printing in tide tables.

When a tide enters shallow water it suffers distortion. The crests tend
to overtake the troughs. If, for the moment, the tide in a shallow estuary,
for example, be looked upon as a wave travelling up the river, the shape
of the original simple harmonic wave (curve I, Fig. 23) is distorted to
the shape of curve II.

Curve II can be obtained from curve I by adding curve III to it.
It will be observed that curve III has half the period of curve I. Thus,
if curve I represented a semi-diurnal tide, curve III would represent a
quarter diurnal tide. Curve III itself is asymmetrical and can be further

analysed giving sixth diurnal and higher species. Astronomical cycles introduce periodicities into the tides of semi-diurnal and slower frequencies. Shallow water introduces periodicities of higher frequency. These have to be allowed for in forecasting the tides at many ports. The general effect of these terms of higher frequency is that the tide runs in quickly and runs out slowly. The time between low water and high water is shorter than that between high water and low water. The incoming tidal currents are more rapid than the outgoing unless there is a large volume of fresh water descending the estuary.

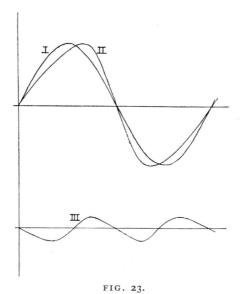

FIG. 23.

Thus a large number of constituent oscillations has to be included to obtain an accurate representation of the tidal fluctuations in the height of the sea at a given place. Forecasts are based on the analysis into these constituents of a long series of observations, of at least a year's duration if possible. The task of reducing the observations, which for a year may number about 9,000 items, is a laborious one, although ingenious methods of computation to isolate the components have been devised. The two principal constituents are known as M_2 and S_2, the semi-diurnal tides of the moon and sun respectively. In naming the constituents, the subscript 2 refers to semi-diurnal tides, the subscript 1 to diurnal tides, a to annual and $S.a$ to semi-annual components, etc. Periodic fluctuations, such as that which occurs because of variations in the moon's distance, are taken account of by having two components of nearly the same frequency which 'beat' together in the correct period. In the case of the variation in the moon's distance, these components are known as N_2 and L_2. Instead of the frequency, the 'speed number' of the oscillation is given. If the oscillation be written $A \cos (\omega t + \phi)$, the speed number is ω and it is usually expressed in degrees per mean solar hour. The speed number of M_2 is $28 \cdot 9841°$ per hour, that of S_2 is $30 \cdot 000°$ per hour. The components N_2 and L_2 have speed numbers $28 \cdot 4397$ and $29 \cdot 5285$ respectively. The diurnal tides, caused by the declination of the sun and the moon, are represented by K_1, with a speed number of $15 \cdot 0411°$ per hour, O_1 with a speed number of $13 \cdot 9430°$ per hour and P_1 with a speed number of $14 \cdot 9589°$ per hour. The component K_1 is common to both lunar and solar diurnal tides. It combines with O_1 to take account of variations in the moon's declination and with P_1 to take account of variations in the sun's declination.

CHAPTER III

The Tides as Observed

How far does the equilibrium theory of the tides fit observation? It is capable, as we have seen, of furnishing explanations of many of the phenomena which are observed. The general approximation of the times of high and low water to a fixed relation to the times of the passage of the sun and the moon across the meridian can be understood on the theory. So can the occurrence of spring and neap tides with a period of a lunar month. The periods of the constituent components of

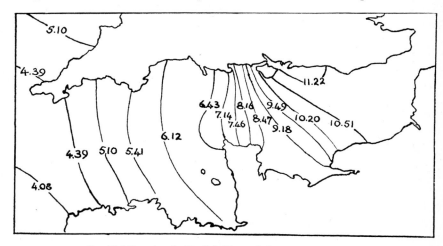

FIG. 24.—*Co-tidal lines for the English Channel, based upon the Ordnance Survey Map and Admiralty Chart No. 5058, with the permission of the Controller of H.M. Stationery Office and of the Hydrographer of the Navy. Crown Copyright reserved.*

the tides is forecast with considerable accuracy. The behaviour of the sea at given localities, however, displays features which entail taking account of many other factors.

Fig. 24 shows the time of high water for the English Channel for a given time of passage of the moon across the meridian at Greenwich. The lines join places where high water occurs at the same time and are known as co-tidal lines. It will be observed that high water occurs first in the west and it then proceeds up channel, taking place at Ventnor in the Isle of Wight some 6 hours later. At first sight this looks like a progressive tidal wave of the equilibrium type, but, of course, the world turns from west to east and the equilibrium tide travels round the world from east to west. The wave in the western English Channel thus travels in the opposite direction to the equilibrium tide. Furthermore, from Ventnor to Dover high water occurs within about 10 minutes of the same time all along the English coast. A similar state of affairs occurs in the Irish Sea. Co-tidal lines for this area are shown in Fig. 25.

FIG. 25.—*Co-tidal lines for the Irish Sea, based upon the Ordnance Survey Map and Admiralty Chart No. 5058, with the permission of the Controller of H.M. Stationery Office and of the Hydrographer of the Navy. Crown Copyright reserved.*

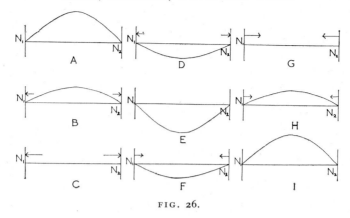

FIG. 26.

High tide occurs progressively later, proceeding up St. George's Channel. At Holyhead it is about $5\frac{1}{2}$ hours later than at Land's End. From Hoylake all round the coast to as far as the Mull of Galloway, however, high water occurs simultaneously to within a matter of 10 minutes or thereabouts. Clearly the water in the Irish Sea is heaving up and down in unison, and the same thing is true for the eastern end of the English Channel. In fact, both seas rise and fall almost together, but that doubtless depends upon the fact that the length and depth of the two arms of the sea connecting them to the place where they join off Land's End are such as to introduce a similar lag in each oscillation.

Tides in more or less enclosed seas, and in gulfs, are of the nature of standing oscillations such as occur in organ pipes in the case of sound waves. The surface which the sea would assume in the case of such an oscillation is illustrated diagrammatically in Fig. 26, $A \ldots H$ for eight successive times. High water occurs simultaneously at all

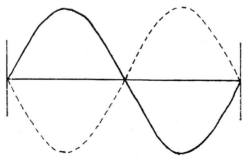

FIG. 27.

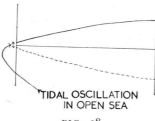

TIDAL OSCILLATION
IN OPEN SEA

FIG. 28.

points between N_1 and N_2, the range of the tide being a maximum in the centre and decreasing to zero at the points N_1 and N_2 themselves, which are consequently known as nodes or nodal points. The arrows represent tidal currents. These are always zero in the centre of the oscillating water and are a maximum at the nodes. They are zero everywhere at the instant of high and low water and reach their maximum values half-way through this period.

The amplitude of the oscillation would be expected to be greatest if the natural period of oscillation of the sea coincided with the main period of the tides of just over 12 hours. Smaller seas might be expected to oscillate in their fundamental period, as in Fig. 26, while larger ones might oscillate in a number of loops, the period of each loop corresponding to the main tidal period. Figs. 26 and 27 are drawn to correspond theoretically to a sea such as the Irish Sea, which, though enclosed, is open at both ends. The ends correspond to N_1 and N_2 and here the tidal currents are a maximum. The Straits of Magellan are similarly open at both ends and the waters oscillate in a complicated way under the influence of the ocean tides. Gulfs, such as Long Island Sound, the Bay of Fundy and also very approximately the English Channel, possess one open end and resonate in a similar manner to the

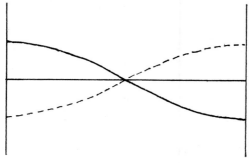

FIG. 29.

oscillation in water level occurring in the sea outside. Oscillation in a gulf is illustrated diagrammatically in Fig. 28. To respond in a single loop to a certain period, a gulf, therefore, has to be of only half the length of that of a sea open at both ends and of the same depth. Oscillation in a totally enclosed sea would have its node in the middle, as in Fig. 29. Currents are necessarily zero at right angles to a shore and so nodes cannot occur at the ends. In this figure the oscillation at the mouth of the gulf has been indicated. There will be similar oscillations at the mouths of the seas, represented in Figs. 26 and 27, but they have been omitted to simplify the figures.

The lengths of a sea or gulf which resonate with a fundamental period of 12 hours depend upon the depth. They are shown in the following table, the lengths for a sea connected at both ends to the ocean being double the corresponding length for a gulf open at one end only.

TABLE I

Resonant Lengths Possessing a Period of 12 hours

Depth in Fathoms	Resonant Length of Gulf open at one end miles	Resonant Length of Sea open at both ends miles
12	87	175
25	123	247
50	175	349
100	247	494
200	349	698
500	552	1,104
1,000	780	1,561
2,000	1,104	2,207

If the gulf or sea resonates in two or more loops the corresponding lengths have obviously to be multiplied by two or more, corresponding to the number of loops. If the periodic time is to be doubled, as would occur in a sea or gulf resonating to a diurnal component of the tide, instead of the semi-diurnal as indicated in the table, the length has also to be doubled. Thus a gulf of depth 50 fathoms and 349 miles in length would resonate with a period of 24 hours. When resonance occurs the amplitude of the oscillations of the water level in the gulf or strait can be very large.

It will be shown in a later chapter that the velocity of a wave travelling in water, the depth H of which is small compared with the wavelength, is given by $\sqrt{gH}$, in which g is the acceleration of gravity. The length of a gulf which resonates in a single loop is a quarter of the wavelength λ of the tidal wave. Since the period, T, of a wave is the time it takes to travel a wavelength, its velocity will be $\dfrac{\lambda}{T}$. Equating this to $\sqrt{gH}$ we have

$\dfrac{\lambda}{T} = \sqrt{gH}$, giving $T = \dfrac{\lambda}{\sqrt{gH}}$. If the resonant length of the sea or gulf

is L we shall have further that $L = \dfrac{\lambda}{4}$ in the case of a gulf and $\dfrac{\lambda}{2}$ in the

case of a sea, so that the natural periods are respectively

$$T = \frac{4L}{\sqrt{gH}} \text{ in the case of a gulf open at one end}$$

$$T = \frac{2L}{\sqrt{gH}} \text{ in the case of a sea open at both ends.}$$

Thus the length of that part of the English Channel from the Isle of Wight to Dover, which we have seen oscillates in unison, is about 120 miles and its depth is of the order of 25 fathoms, which corresponds to the figures given for a gulf in the second line of Table I. Long Island Sound, New York, is about 80 miles long and has an average depth of about 11 fathoms. The Bay of Fundy is of similar length and depth and a standing oscillation is again set up with a node at the entrance. The length and depth of water in the Bristol Channel is also similar.

Resonant oscillations in a gulf would be expected to increase the amplitude of the tidal oscillation and this, in fact, does occur. The great range of the tide in the Bristol Channel (up to 48 feet) and in the Bay of Fundy (up to 70 feet) is well known. There is also a large range in the Straits of Magellan, which are open at both ends to the ocean. They are about 250 miles long and would be expected to oscillate with maximum amplitude (i.e. an antinode) in the middle and nodes at each end.

In a wave which is advancing the velocity of the water particles is in the direction of motion of the wave under the crest and in the opposite direction under the trough. Tidal streams have thus their greatest velocities at high and low water if the wave of the tide is a travelling one. If the wave of the tide takes the form of a stationary oscillation the tidal streams possess their maximum velocities at half tide, as has already been seen in Fig. 26.

Tidal streams, like winds, are affected by the rotational motion of the earth. That is to say they obey Buys Ballot's law and are deflected to the right in the northern hemisphere and to the left in the southern. In a narrow channel movement in a direction across the channel is necessarily limited. The tendency for the tidal currents to be deflected is counteracted by the hydrostatic pressure set up by the gradient of the surface of the sea, as water piles up on the right-hand coast. In the case of the English Channel, the motion of whose water is largely oscillatory,

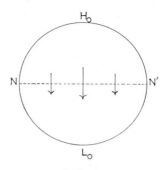

FIG. 30.

with the currents forming between the times of high and low water, and running up channel in the period preceding high water and down channel in the period preceding low water, the effect of the right-handed deflection is to increase the height of high water on the French coast and the height of low water on the English coast. Tidal ranges, therefore, tend to be greater along the French than the English coast.

In seas which are not very narrow, in which transverse streams are capable of being developed, the effect of the rotational motion of the earth is to induce a rotary wave motion in the sea. Consider a circular basin (Fig. 30) in which there is no rotation and where there is an oscillation producing high water at H_0 and low water at L_0. As high water subsides at H_0 and low water rises at L_0, currents in the direction of the arrows set in across the nodal line NN'. If there is rotation the tendency to turn to the right will be counterbalanced by a pressure gradient developed in the water, producing a new high water at H_1 and a low water at L_1.

The gradient from H_1 to L_1 must reach its maximum when the

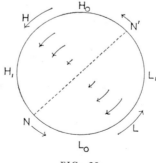

FIG. 31.

currents attain their maximum velocity, which is when the water at H_0 and L_0 has attained its mean level. The result is a travelling wave which rotates round the basin, as in Fig. 32. The current is in the direction of propagation of the wave under the crest and against this direction under the trough. Since crest and trough are rotating, the direction of the currents in both sectors is the same. The line NN' corresponding to zero displacement of the surface rotates with the wave. The nodal line which exists in the absence of gyration is thus reduced to a single point O (Fig. 32). Such a point of constant zero displacement is known as an amphidromic point.

Three such amphidromic points occur in the North Sea. The most northerly lies just off the coast of southern Norway. Along this coast the tidal range is very small. This is a further illustration of the tendency for the greatest tidal ranges to occur on the right-hand side of a channel

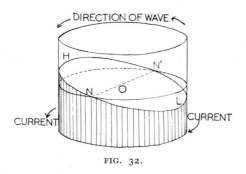

FIG. 32.

leading to an enclosed sea. A second amphidromic point occurs off the coast of Denmark and the third between the coasts of Suffolk and Holland.

The reason that amphidromic points do not develop in the English Channel is probably that it is too narrow. Nevertheless, there is a tendency for one to form in the region of the Isle of Wight, as may be seen by the crowding of the co-tidal lines, which appear as if radiating from a point to the north of the Island. Another amphidromic point occurs off the Kintyre peninsula on the west coast of Scotland, and there is a degenerate one, similar to that near the Isle of Wight, just inside the Irish coast in County Wicklow.

The measurement of the height of tides at sea is a very difficult process. Even in narrow waters an indirect method, calculating the surface gradient from tidal streams, which are easier to measure, is employed. In the oceans information is practically restricted to observation on islands. Various attempts to draw co-tidal lines for the oceans

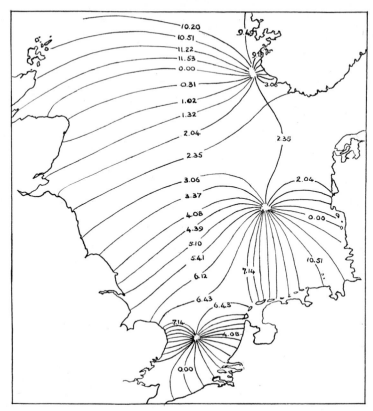

FIG. 33.—*Co-tidal lines for the North Sea, based upon the Ordnance Survey Map and Admiralty Chart No. 5058, with the permission of the Controller of H.M. Stationery Office and of the Hydrographer of the Navy. Crown Copyright reserved.*

have been made but the result is inevitably rather speculative. Nevertheless, the general picture of the tides as caused by the oscillation of various bodies of water under the tide-raising forces of the sun and the moon remains. These bodies of water execute forced oscillations in time with the forces which excite them. The amplitude of the oscillations produced will depend upon how near they are to resonance with any of the harmonic constituents of the tide-raising forces.

CHAPTER IV

Tidal Bores

NEAR the sea in an estuary the times of the ebb and flow of the tide are approximately equal. Higher up, particularly if the estuary narrows, this is no longer the case. The period of the ebb becomes longer and that of the flow shorter. The velocity of the currents in the ebb is correspondingly less than in the flow, unless there is a large quantity of fresh water descending the river to mask the effect. The shape of the tide curve for such rivers is sketched in Fig. 34.

The mass of water in the estuary acquires considerable momentum as a result of the tidal currents and this is reversed at each change of the tide. Correspondingly large forces and time in which they can act are required to bring this about. These forces are provided by the changes in gradient of the water surface as the tide in the sea rises and

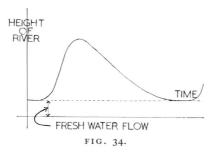

FIG. 34.

falls. It is when the momentum of the incoming water is concentrated into a narrow front by the gradual narrowing of the channel or by a rise in the bed of the river, or both, that tidal bores are formed. A more detailed discussion will be given in Chapter V.

A tidal bore consists of a body of water advancing up the river with the incoming tide and possessing a well-defined front separating it from the still or slowly ebbing water into which it advances. The front takes the form of a wave or series of waves, often breaking and foaming. Behind it the level of the water is higher, and often considerably higher, than it is in front. On those English rivers in which bores form the difference may be as great as 4 feet as the bore passes. The water level, of course, continues to rise rapidly after the bore has passed until high water is reached.

As the advancing tide travels into the still water ahead of it, it gives it forward momentum and gathers it up, joining it to itself. The tidal bore thus travels faster than the tidal current which brings the incoming tide up river. If, as is usually the case, the height of the bore is small compared with the depth of the river, the velocity of the bore is large compared with the velocity of the water which follows it. This is illustrated in Fig. 35 diagrammatically. The actual profile of the bore on the Severn and Trent is similar to the curve sketched in Fig. 36.

The bore on the River Severn is the best known example of the phenomenon in England. It has been the subject of a long series of observations. It was reported on in 1849 in a survey of the River Severn by Captain Beechey. He wrote:

'The highest tide of the year rolled up the Severn on the 1st December. There was about 2 feet of water above the ordinary summer level in the river, and the morning was calm and favourable to the phenomenon. The stream at low water ran down at the rate of $2\frac{1}{2}$ miles

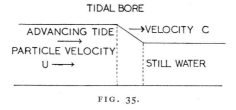

FIG. 35.

(geographical) per hour, until the time when the bore came rolling up the river with a breast from 5 to 6 feet high at the sides and 3 feet 6 inches in the centre. The stream turned up the instant after the bore passed, and ran at the rate of $3\frac{3}{4}$ miles per hour, which was about half the average rate of the bore, the speed of which varies from 12 to 7 miles per hour, averaging 8 between Stonebench and Gloucester.'

The Severn bore was described by Dr Vaughan Cornish[1] in 1902 and by the staff of the Admiralty survey during 1926–7. Its characteristics were also investigated by means of a model of the Severn Estuary, the behaviour of which corresponded, with considerable accuracy, to that observed in the actual bore in the river. It was described by A. H. Gibson.[2]

Describing the bore of September 29th 1901 at Stonebench, Dr Cornish wrote:

'The bore was heard at 9 a.m. a few seconds before its appearance round the bend of the river, at a distance of 513 yards. . . . The height

[1] Dr Vaughan Cornish, *Geographical Journal*, Vol. 19, 1902, p. 52; Vol. 29, 1907, p. 28.
[2] *A Tidal Model of the Severn Estuary*, A. H. Gibson.

PLATES V and VI.—*Stages of the passage of the Mascaret at Caudebec-en-Caux.* (*Photos by Miss Mary Ennever.*)

of the wave then I estimate at from 3 feet to 3 feet 6 inches and the height at the sides of the river 4 to 5 feet. At the jetty or breakwater, of which one post already referred to was visible beyond the osiers, the bore suddenly sent a sheet of water up to a height of 7 or 8 feet but, recovering itself in a moment, the wave came on with a front still smooth and unbroken, its inverted image perfectly mirrored by the smooth water ahead of it. The speed of the bore was about 13½ statute miles per hour. High water occurred 56 minutes after the passage of the bore, the total rise being 8 feet 6½ inches. The height of the water then above ordnance datum was several feet higher than high water of even a 40-foot tide at Portishead. The current continued to flow up the river for 31 minutes after high water.'

The last two sentences are particularly interesting and show the effect of the momentum of the water in carrying it to a greater height

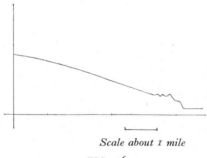

Scale about 1 mile

FIG. 36.

than that from which it could have started and in producing a lag between occurrence of high and low waters and the tidal currents which give rise to them. The current was actually flowing upstream for as long as 31 minutes after the level of water had started to fall. It did not reverse at the moment of high water.

Though it occasionally forms below Severn Bridge only to vanish again, the bore begins definitely some little distance above this and its height depends very much on the configuration of the Noose and Frampton sands.

No bores form on neap tides. The first noticeable bore occurs on about the eighth tide before spring, and bores may be expected for about four days on each side of spring tides. As a general guide to those wishing to observe the phenomenon, a tide of at least 30 feet at Sharpness is required to produce a bore worth looking at. The highest tides at this point reach over 32 feet. The higher the tide the greater the bore,

D

other things being equal. In the Severn estuary the highest tides occur two or three days after new and full moon.

From its inception above Severn Bridge, the bore increases in height and attains its maximum between Framilode and Stonebench. Thereafter the height slowly diminishes towards Gloucester, though it travels beyond that city. The bore can be observed well at Minsterworth on the right bank of the river or at Framilode and Stonebench on the left.

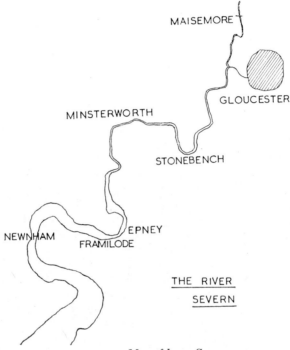

FIG. 37.—*Map of lower Severn.*

In a car the same bore can easily be seen twice, first at Framilode or Epney and then at Stonebench. If traffic conditions in Gloucester are favourable, it can even be seen a third time from the bridge which carries the Ross road over the river, or a little higher up at Maisemore. At Minsterworth and Stonebench there is a shallow stretch which causes the wave to break and renders it more spectacular.

The speed at which the bore travels depends upon the depth of water in the river and on the height of the bore. Thus it is faster when the river is full than when it is low, a factor which should be allowed for when timing one's arrival to see it. The higher the bore also, the faster it travels. The height and speed of the bore are slightly greater on tides preceding the highest spring tide than on the corresponding tide afterwards. This is thought to be due to the deposition of material carried upstream on the fast-moving inflowing tide at spring. Flood water flowing down the river tends to increase the speed of the bore, by reason of increased depth, and to diminish its height.

The speed of the bore between Newnham and Framilode is from 7 to 8 miles per hour. Above Framilode it increases to 12 to 13 miles per hour.

The bore passes Framilode about 30 minutes, and Stonebench about 70 minutes, after the time of high water at Avonmouth. These times are subject to variation, not only because of variation in the depth of water in the river but also because the speed is affected by the wind. This latter effect is not so much a direct action on the bore itself as an indirect action by reason of the influence the wind has on the height of the tide and depth of the river.

Bores on the Severn rarely exceed a height of 4 feet in mid-stream, though the height is greater near the banks. Wild fowl have learnt the wisdom of meeting the bore in mid-stream and not near the sides, where the buffeting can be much more severe. Nevertheless, the writer has seen a pair of swans submerged by the bore even though they were in mid-stream. They remained under water for a very considerable period—of the order of 30 seconds in one case and longer in the other. It is doubtful if the immersion could have been voluntary under these circumstances, even though after emergence and some flapping of wings they appeared to settle down to a normal existence almost immediately, but much farther upstream than the point at which they disappeared. The bore can be ridden in a boat kept head on to the wave.

From the point of view of this book an important interest in tidal bores attaches to a simple theoretical examination of their velocity of propagation. In Chapter V it will be shown that a bore of height h in a river of depth H before the arrival of the bore, travels with a velocity given by

$$c = \sqrt{\frac{2g(H + h)^2}{2H + h}} \qquad . \qquad . \qquad . \qquad . \qquad 1$$

g being the acceleration due to gravity.

This applies to the case of the propagation of the bore into still water. If before the bore arrives the river has a velocity of v feet per second downstream, the velocity of the bore becomes

$$c = \sqrt{\frac{2g(H + h)^2}{2H + h}} - v \qquad . \qquad . \qquad . \qquad 2$$

a formula which is in close agreement with observation. If the height of the bore is small compared with the depth of the river the velocity reduces to

$$c = \sqrt{gH} \quad . \quad . \quad . \quad . \quad . \quad 3$$

At Stonebench the depth of the Severn is commonly about 10 feet and the velocity of the bore according to Equation 3 would be 18 feet per second, which is equivalent to about $12\frac{1}{2}$ miles per hour, a value close to that actually observed.

Those who live near the Severn speak of the bore as 'the tide' and do not appear to use the term bore much at all. Usborne Moore reports that the Chinese name for the bore on the Chien Tang Kiang is Chau— the tide. Sometimes they speak of it at Haining as Chau Dau—the Great Tide. The same phenomenon on the Trent is known as the aegir. It is similar in magnitude and speed to the bore on the Severn. It can be seen anywhere from Gunness, near Scunthorpe, to Gainsborough, and forms at times near spring tides, as on the River Severn. There is an extensive use of the Trent by barge traffic, whereas the Severn is not used by shipping above Sharpness. Barges ride the aegir without difficulty. In the lower reaches of the River Trent the main wave is sometimes followed by a second, known as the 'second shove', some 3 to 5 minutes after the first has passed. This sometimes reaches as far as Stockwith but not Gainsborough. Its cause is probably to be found in the division of the channel of the river by sandbanks so that two aegirs are generated. These have different distances to go and probably travel in channels of different depths so that they follow one another up the river.

Bores on rivers find their mention in literature. The aegir on the Trent occurs in *The Mill on the Floss*. The tide in the Solway Firth which comes in over wide stretches of sand is not a river bore in the strict sense of the term but is nevertheless a similar phenomenon. It was described by Sir Walter Scott in *Redgauntlet*. Darsie Latimer in his letter to Alan Fairford describes how he 'crossed over the open downs which divided me from the margin of the Solway. When I reached', he wrote, 'the banks of the great estuary, which are here very bare and exposed, the waters had receded from the large and level space of sand, through which a stream, now feeble and fordable, found its way to the ocean.' Seeing horsemen spearing salmon in the narrow waters he ventured forward a considerable space upon the sands. The horsemen began to make for the shore but Darsie Latimer lingered on the sands meditating. He relates how his 'steps were arrested by the sound of a horse galloping; and as I turned', he continued, 'the rider (the same fisherman whom I had formerly distinguished) called out to me, in an

abrupt manner, "Soho, brother! you are too late for Bowness tonight
—the tide will make presently" '. Darsie did not answer for a while.
' "Are you deaf?" he added, "or are you mad, or have you a mind for
the next world?" "I am a stranger", I answered, "and had no other
purpose than looking in at the fishing—I am about to return to the side
I came from."

' "Best make haste then," said he. "He that dreams on the bed of
Solway may wake in the next world. The sky threatens a blast that will
bring in the waves three feet abreast."

'So saying, he turned his horse and rode off while I began to walk
back towards the Scottish shore, a little alarmed at what I had heard;
for the tide advances with such rapidity upon these fatal sands, that
well-mounted horsemen lay aside hopes of safety if they see its white
surge advancing while they are yet at a distance from the bank.'

In England bores form in a number of other rivers though they attain
no great magnitude. There is one on the River Kent in the south of
Westmorland. Another forms on the Mersey and there is a small bore
on the River Parrett at Bridgwater. Though on the Parrett the bore
itself is only a few inches in height, it generates a very striking pattern
of waves on the calm surface of the narrow river by reflection from the
near-vertical banks. On the passage of the bore the surface of the water
rises about 2 feet and there is the same reversal in the direction of the
current as occurs on the Severn and Trent. Just below the bridge which
carries the main street over the river there is also a shallow patch
extending across the river, which causes the wave to slow down and
break, even though it is only of small amplitude. Once over the shallow
section the bore reforms into a series of smooth waves progressing
upstream. The Trent and Mersey bores are illustrated in Plates 1 and 2.

A much more formidable bore forms on the lower Seine between
Rouen and the sea. It is known as the Mascaret and it has a long series
of accidents and drownings to its credit and is well feared. Victor Hugo,
who lived at Villequier, lost his eldest daughter and her husband Charles
Vacquier in the Mascaret of the 4th September 1843, drowned in front
of his house. He wrote a poem about it called *A Villequier*, expressing
the grief of a father at his loss. It does not describe or say anything
about the Mascaret itself, however.

The Mascaret reaches its greatest development at Caudebec-en-
Caux, about half-way from Le Havre to Rouen. From there it travels
almost to Rouen, its amplitude gradually decreasing. The Seine is a
much deeper river than either the Severn above Sharpness or the Trent.
Ocean-going ships use it regularly to get to Rouen. The Mascaret therefore travels faster than the bores in these two English rivers. Its speed
is about 15 miles per hour. To keep up with the wave in the centre of

the river, which is of small amplitude only in itself, the waves near the banks have to be of correspondingly greater amplitude. The phenomenon thus takes the form of very large waves travelling along each bank with little visible elsewhere. Caudebec-en-Caux is on the outside of a loop in the Seine which might be thought to bring the deep-water channel to that side of the river and thus decrease the amplitude of the wave. The reverse, however, is actually the case and the wave appears

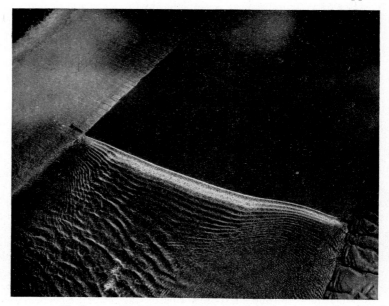

PLATE I.—*The bore on the Mersey; aerial photograph taken between Warrington and Liverpool. The river at low tide is about 350 ft. wide. Near the top of the picture is a small buoy around which ripples can be seen, showing that the direction of flow before the wave arrives is towards the wave. (Photo by Airviews (M/c) Limited.)*

to reach a maximum opposite the quay in the town. The explanation of this is not obvious unless it be that reflection from the bank has something to do with it. Higher up the river at La Bouille, however, the reverse happens. There the wave hugs the inner side of the bend and there is very little visible at all on the outside. At Caudebec a fair-sized wave runs along the opposite bank (i.e. on the inside of the loop) but at La Bouille the wave on the outside of the loop (which at Caudebec swamps the quay) is only a matter of inches high. Apart from the fact that the Mascaret is of rather smaller amplitude at La Bouille than it

PLATE 2.—*Two views of the aegir on the Trent. The upper photograph (taken at Gainsborough) shows the increase of amplitude of the wave in the shallow water close to the banks. In the lower picture, taken from behind at Morton Corner, the wall of water is seen advancing up the river.*

is at Caudebec, the two cases appear quite comparable. It is difficult to know what effect any dredging of the river may have had.

The amplitude of the Mascaret is said to have been decreased through works carried out to improve the waterway, but at Caudebec the wave can still reach a height of 24 feet if the tide is aided by a strong westerly wind. Formerly a bore formed on every tide but now the phenomenon is only of any magnitude on about four tides each side of the springs. However, when it does form, it regularly breaks over the quay at Caudebec. 'La vague colossale deferle sur les Rives, éclaboussant copieusement les curieux les plus téméraires, créant même des accidents—en 1961 un ménage Havrais s'est noyé emporté par le flot qui les avait cueillis sur la rive.'[1]

The frontispiece to this book is a photograph of the Mascaret on the morning of September 16th 1962, taken from mid-stream, on board the ferry. (See also Colour Plates V and VI.) It was not one of the greatest in height, the conditions being calm and the weather fair, a not altogether unwelcome aid to photography.

The Mascaret is one of the sights at Caudebec and regularly attracts a sizable body of visitors. At night the wave is illuminated by floodlight. This wave is large enough near the banks and the change in water level great enough for quite substantial vessels, such as the ferry which is capable of carrying a dozen or so heavy lorries, to find it necessary to ride the bore in mid-stream. Tidal currents in the Seine are very strong. They are, of course, used by shipping proceeding to and from Rouen. The gradients, however, are small. Rouen is only about 15 feet above sea level. The river has eroded its way through the chalk hills and its flood plain is bounded by high cliffs, producing a very attractive landscape. Its banks are not encumbered by industry. Whether the Mascaret has had anything to do with this preservation of the countryside is perhaps an open question.

Tidal bores occur widely in other parts of the world. There is a large one, of some 4 or 5 feet in height, in the Petitcodiac River in New Brunswick. The high tides in the Bay of Fundy have already been remarked upon. In the Bay of St Michel the tide runs over the large expanse of sand, left dry at low water, with great rapidity, just as it does in the Solway Firth. The wave of a tidal bore can travel along a river of any depth. Occasions when it travels over dry sandbanks may be considered to be the limiting case when the depth of the river has decreased to vanishing point. It is the sudden change of water level which occurs as the tide flows in which is the characteristic feature. Probably the most famous of all tidal bores is that on the Chien Tang Kiang river in China, which was studied by Commander (later Admiral)

[1] Syndicat d'initiative de Caudebec-en-Caux.

W. Usborne Moore in 1888 and 1892. He reported the height as from
8 to 11 feet, which, if in the middle of the river, would make it one of
the largest. According to his account 1¾ million tons of water were
carried up the river per minute by a current which reached a speed of
10 knots. Admiral Moore appears to have taken it for granted that the
highest part of a tidal bore would occur in the middle of the river
where the incoming tide meets the main outgoing current of the river.
His estimates of the height of the wave indeed place the highest point

BORE OF THE 10ᵗʰ OCTOBER 1892.

PLATE 3.—*Usborne Moore's sketch of the bore on the Chien Tang Kiang, taken
from his photograph.*

in the deepest part of the river channel. In this he may have been
influenced by theoretical ideas about how a bore is caused—he evidently
subscribed to the view that a bore is due to 'a conflict' between the
incoming tide and the outflowing river. However, whatever may have
been the actual height in the centre of the river it was certainly very
considerable. Drawings based on photographs which he took with much
difficulty with the early form of camera, seem to indicate a uniform
height across the river. One of Moore's drawings is reproduced in
Plate 3. Bores, however, have their greatest height by the banks where

the water is shallowest, though with the very vigorous bore in the Chien Tang Kiang the difference may well have been small. Usborne Moore describes how Chinese junks shelter in specially constructed bays (Plate 4) until the bore has passed and then emerge to take advantage of the current. He said that on one occasion 'nine junks came up behind with sails set, but regardless of the wind, of which indeed there was none, and entered the river at great speed'. On another occasion 'no less than 30 junks swept up in the after rush and passed Haining with all sails set but their bows pointing in every direction, several proceeding stern first at a rate of 10 knots towards the city of Hang Chau'.

PLATE 4.—*Bore shelter for junks. Haining. (Sketch by Usborne Moore.)*

It is not a difficult matter to study the properties of tidal bores and waves in shallow water by means of simple models. The relation between the velocity of propagation and the depth of water can easily be elucidated experimentally. The simple theory of this relation will be postponed until the next chapter, but since so many of the properties of waves in shallow water depend upon it many will welcome a direct demonstration of it. The non-mathematical reader may prefer to rely upon the results of experiment and omit the theoretical considerations altogether.

All that is required is a rough wooden box about 6 feet long by 1 foot wide and 1 foot deep. It need not be watertight since by far the simplest method of construction is to line the box with plastic sheeting. This should not be cut to fit the ends, but folded over instead, so that a watertight skin is produced. A paddle made by attaching a piece of wood, which loosely fits the cross-section of the box, to a handle, is required to urge the water forward. Plate 5 shows a photograph of such a simple tank used by the author to obtain the results described in subsequent sections of this book. Water is placed in the trough to a convenient depth. With a box having the dimensions suggested a few centimetres of water is suitable. A bore can be generated by moving the paddle forward at a steady speed. It will be observed immediately that the bore travels at a greater speed than the piston, thus confirming the statement that the velocity of the bore exceeds that of the current

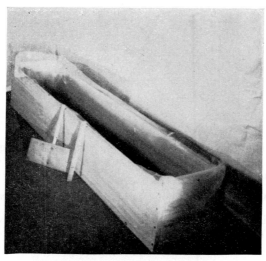

PLATE 5.—*Simple wave tank. It consists of a simple wooden box lined with poly-thene sheeting. By the side are the paddle for generating waves and the depth gauge.*

of water which follows it. A wave can be generated by a limited move-ment of the paddle. Both bore and wave follow the same law of pro-pagation, as will be shown in a later chapter.

The tank shown in Plate 5 has the dimensions suggested in the previous paragraph. The time taken by a bore or wave to travel the length of the trough can be measured by a stop-watch. In the case of the waves it will be observed that they are reflected when they reach the ends and they will continue to travel backwards and forwards many times. By timing a wave over several transits of the trough the accuracy of measurement is considerably increased. If one wishes to verify that the velocity of waves is proportional to the square root of the depth it is important to work with waves of small amplitude (only to which this relation applies).

PLATE 7.—*Waves travelling down tubes of different diameters. All three were generated simultaneously. That in the wide tube has travelled farthest. All will arrive at the far end simultaneously. The lengths of the tubes are proportional to the square roots of the diameters.*

behind the front of the bore) and the depth of water used was such that they were covered to a depth of a couple of centimetres. The increase in the amplitude of the wave of the bore over the bricks is most marked.

A rather more elegant method of demonstrating that a bore or wave in shallow water travels with a speed proportional to the square root of the depth, consists in taking a number of glass tubes of various diameters. Each tube is filled half full with water, and if a little fluorescene is added it makes the observation easier. Lengths of tube proportional to the square roots of the diameters are marked on each tube from one end. The tubes are closed with bungs at each end and they are mounted one above the other in a rack. Inside each tube is a third loosely fitting bung attached to a wire to act as a piston for the generation of waves. The wires are brought out through holes in the end bungs of the tubes. The pistons are arranged near the marks and the wires connected to them are held in one hand so that waves may be started simultaneously in all the tubes. When waves are sent down the tubes together in this way, it will be seen that they arrive at the far ends simultaneously, demonstrating again that the velocity of a wave in shallow water is proportional to the square root of the depth. A diagram of the apparatus is given in Fig. 39, and a photograph of the actual apparatus in Plate 7.

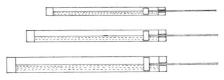

FIG. 39.

In the photograph the water has again been coloured with potassium permanganate to make it show up. Waves have been generated simultaneously in all three tubes by moving the pistons towards the left-hand ends. Already the wave in the large tube at the bottom has travelled farther than that in the next tube above it and the wave in that tube, in turn, has travelled farther than that in the smallest tube at the top. All the waves will arrive at the left-hand ends at the same time.

This variation of the velocity of a wave in shallow water as the depth of the water changes is a most important phenomenon. The expression $\sqrt{gD}$ is one which will be found to crop up continually in all sorts of places in connection with the movement of liquids. Upon it depends a large number of the properties of waves as we observe them on beaches at the seaside. The next chapter will be devoted to a deduction of this relation on the basis of very simple mechanical principles.

CHAPTER V

An Elementary Theory of Tidal Bores

MUCH of the properties of waves on water can be understood on the basis of very simple considerations involving little mathematics. Waves are primarily things which affect the surface of water and we shall confine ourselves to consideration of the motion of particles on the surface itself. This will simplify the study very considerably and yet, at the same time, will furnish many of the most important conclusions. A convenient starting-point for this study is provided by the tidal bore which, in outline, is basically very simple, and we shall begin with that. It will occupy the present chapter and the development of wave theory from it will follow in succeeding chapters.

The basic mechanics which is needed is very slight. We shall require the expression for the work done by force—the product of the size of the force and the distance through which it moves—in the particular case of the lifting of a mass m through a height h. The work done is the product of the weight—mg—and the height h, that is mgh. We shall need the expression for the kinetic energy of a body of mass m moving with velocity v, namely, $\dfrac{mv^2}{2}$. This is the work it can do against a force which brings it to rest, and it is also the work which must be provided to make the body move with velocity v, starting from rest. Thus when a body of mass m falls through a height of h feet, gravity performs an amount of work, mgh, on the body which as a result acquires an equivalent kinetic energy, so that we have, in this case

$$\frac{mv^2}{2} = mgh \qquad . \qquad . \qquad . \qquad . \qquad . \qquad 4$$

Fluids move under the action of forces just as do solid bodies. In their case, however, there is a pressure at each point of the fluid which acts on each particle inside, and this has to be taken account of in addition to forces arising from such causes as gravity. This is where our simplification of considering only particles on the surface eases matters. At the surface of a liquid the pressure is atmospheric. It is thus the same on both the front and back of any surface particle and does not tend to accelerate or retard it. It therefore plays no part in our considerations. We have only to take account of gravity and the varying kinetic energy of the liquid particles. There are, of course, retarding forces arising from the viscosity of the liquid, but these are small in

PLATE VII.—*Spilling breakers.*

PLATE VIII.—*Spilling breakers.*

the case of water and other liquids which are of interest in connection with surface waves. They will be neglected in the present treatment and indeed are neglected also for a great deal of the time in much more exact mathematical considerations.

There is one further condition which is important and needs consideration. It is that our discussion applies only to steady conditions. That is to say, it applies only to the flow of the liquid in which the velocity of particles, as they pass a given point, always remains the same in both direction and magnitude. As the particle of the liquid flows to different points in space, its velocity, of course, can change in both these respects, but as successive particles pass a given point in space they all assume the same velocity. Under these circumstances the surface of the liquid must remain stationary and so must the streamlines of the flow within the liquid. Now a wave motion is, by its very nature, not a steady motion; but a simple device, originated by Lord Rayleigh, enables it to be reduced to a case of steady motion very easily. It is the

PLATE 8.—*Waves held stationary by an adverse current. The ripples at the top of the waterfall travel at the same speed as the current of water and the pattern remains stationary.*

E

method known as that of the adverse current. We imagine the waves to be propagated against an adverse current of such a speed that the waves are rendered stationary. The liquid is thus carried back through the waves, as in a mill-race, while the undulating surface of the liquid is held fixed. Plate 8 shows the effect of an adverse current at the top of a waterfall.

Under these circumstances, it follows from what has been said that the liquid particles in the surface slide over the waves just as a smooth solid particle would slide over a smooth switchback. In the next chapter we shall see how this fact can lead to a simple mechanical model which helps to give an understanding of one important feature of wave motion in shallow water. In this chapter we shall be concerned with tidal bores, and the motion of a surface particle under the influence of an adverse current which brings the wavefront of the bore to rest, will be only the mounting of a simple step in the water surface.

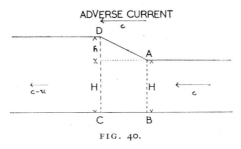

FIG. 40.

Let us superimpose an adverse current to the left, on the conditions depicting the advance of a tidal bore into still water, shown in Fig. 35. The result is given in Fig. 40. Suppose the bore was advancing to the right with velocity c. An adverse current of this velocity will cause the bore to remain stationary. Instead of having still water to the right, as in Fig. 35, we shall now have water flowing to the left with velocity c, as in Fig. 40. To the left of the bore the water particles, instead of advancing with the former particle velocity u to the right, will now travel to the left, but with the reduced velocity $c - u$.

The depth, H, of the river before the arrival of the bore will be known and we want to work out the velocity of a bore of given height h which we, therefore, assume is also known. There are, however, two unknown quantities c and u to be considered. We need, therefore, two conditions to determine them. There are, in fact, two conditions which we can apply, and these suffice to determine both these unknowns. The problem could, of course, have been put the other way round. We might assume that we know the velocity of the tidal current and wish to work out the height of the bore which it would produce, but which way round the problem is put is of little importance.

The two conditions we have available to apply are as follows. The first is that the loss of kinetic energy of a particle of fluid in the surface as it flows up the slope of the bore must be equal to the work done against gravity. That is to say

$$\tfrac{1}{2}mc^2 - \tfrac{1}{2}m(c - u)^2 = mgh \qquad . \qquad . \qquad . \qquad 5$$

The second condition is that as much water must flow away to the left of the stationary bore as arrives from the right, in any time. Consider a section of the river 1 foot wide at AB (Fig. 40). Its depth is H feet and therefore the area of cross-section will be $H.1$ square feet, that is H square feet. A length c feet of water will arrive at this cross-section each second and hence the volume of water crossing the cross-section at AB per second is $H.c$ cubic feet. Similarly the volume of water leaving a similar cross-section 1 foot wide at DC will be $(H + h)(c - u)$.

Therefore $\qquad\qquad Hc = (H + h)(c - u) \qquad . \qquad . \qquad . \qquad 6$

Equations 5 and 6 are two simultaneous equations from which we have to find u and c. Let us multiply out the brackets in Equation 6. We obtain

$$Hc = Hc - Hu + hc - hu$$

or $\qquad\qquad\qquad hc = u(H + h) \qquad . \qquad . \qquad . \qquad . \qquad 7$

Multiplying out the brackets in Equation 5 gives

$$\frac{mc^2}{2} - \frac{mc^2}{2} + mcu - \frac{mu^2}{2} = mgh$$

or $\qquad\qquad\qquad cu - \frac{u^2}{2} = gh \qquad . \qquad . \qquad . \qquad . \qquad 8$

In this chapter we shall make the assumption that the particle velocity is small compared with the velocity of the wave of the bore, so that we may neglect u^2 compared with u. It is not difficult to work out the result without making this assumption, and the extra calculations involved are carried out in Appendix II. Neglecting u^2 Equation 8 becomes

$$cu = gh \qquad . \qquad . \qquad . \qquad . \qquad . \qquad 9$$

From Equation 7 we have

$$u = \frac{hc}{H + h}$$

Substituting this value into Equation 9 we obtain

$$\frac{hc^2}{H + h} = gh$$

giving finally

$$c = \sqrt{g(H + h)} \qquad . \qquad . \qquad . \qquad . \qquad 10$$

This is a most important relation which we shall find cropping up again and again in the study of waves in shallow water. We see that the velocity of a tidal bore depends primarily on the depth of water after the bore has passed, and that it varies as the square root of this depth. The result of the more complete calculations given in Appendix II, in which the term in u^2 in Equation 8 is not neglected, is that

$$c = \sqrt{\frac{(H + h)^2 g}{H + \dfrac{h}{2}}} \qquad . \qquad . \qquad . \qquad . \quad 11$$

Taking the simpler expression of Equation 10, which will hold for bores of small amplitude, we would find that for a river 12 feet deep after the passage of the bore, the velocity is

$$c = \sqrt{32 \times 12} \text{ feet per second}$$
$$= 19 \cdot 6 \text{ feet per second}$$
$$= 13 \cdot 4 \text{ miles per hour}$$

which is in good agreement with the observed velocities of the bore on the Severn, after allowing for the fact that a fresh water current of about 2 miles per hour would reduce the speed to something between 11 and 12 miles per hour.

We also see that the higher the bore the more quickly does it travel. The velocity, depending on the square root of the depth, is not rapidly affected by changes in depth. The above figures, for example, would apply to a bore of height 2 feet entering a channel with water 10 feet deep. If the bore were 4 feet in height the velocity comes out to be only 14·5 miles per hour, giving a net speed of 12·5 miles per hour against a fresh water current of 2 miles per hour.

The run from Newnham to Gloucester is about 15 miles by river, so that at 11·4 miles per hour the bore on the Severn would take 1 hour 18·6 minutes to do the journey, and at 12·5 miles per hour it would take 1 hour 12 minutes. The difference in the time of arrival at Gloucester, caused by variations in the height of the bore from 2 to 4 feet, amounts to only 6½ minutes.

The speeds given by the more accurate Equation 11 are, 14 miles per hour for the 2-foot bore and 15·6 miles per hour for one of 4 feet in height. At these speeds, allowing for an adverse fresh water current of 2 miles per hour as before, the times taken by the bores to travel from Newnham to Gloucester would be 1 hour 15 minutes and 1 hour 6 minutes respectively, the difference amounting to 9 minutes. It is doubtful, however, how far it is really necessary to use the more accurate expression. There are so many uncertain factors, such as variations in the depth of the river, the velocity of the fresh water downstream and the effect of wind, that the estimate can only be of rough value in any case. The velocity of the fresh water reduces the velocities in both cases equally and thus increases the difference in the time taken by the two bores to travel up river. An increase in the depth before the arrival of the bore will decrease both the times of passage and also the difference in the times taken by the two bores to do the journey.

Another phenomenon which the formula for the velocity for the tidal bore helps to explain, is the greater height which a bore attains near the banks of the river than it does in the middle. The depth of the river is rarely the same at all points across a cross-section. Usually it is less near the banks than it is in the middle. A bore, however, travels up a river as a single wave, in spite of the fact that, for a bore of given height, the velocity where the water is shallow is less than where it is deep. The ability to travel as a whole comes about through the height of the bore being greater at the sides than in the middle. As the wave tends to lag behind near to the banks energy is continually transferred to it from the mass of water in the centre. This builds up the amplitude until the whole wave is able to travel forward with the same speed.

Let us consider the case of the bore in the Severn, as before, and suppose that the height of the bore in mid-stream is 2 feet with a depth of water in the river of 10 feet before the bore arrived. Taking the more accurate equation, the velocity of the bore is

$$\sqrt{\frac{(H+h)^2g}{H+\dfrac{h}{2}}} = \sqrt{\frac{(10+2)^2g}{10+1}}$$

$$= \sqrt{\frac{144}{11}g}$$

What height must a bore be if the depth of water in the river before its arrival was only 5 feet, if it is to travel with the same velocity? The velocity in this case would be

$$\sqrt{\frac{(5+h)^2g}{5+\dfrac{h}{2}}}$$

Equating this to the previous value and cancelling g we obtain

$$\frac{(5+h)^2}{5+\dfrac{h}{2}} = \frac{144}{11}$$

The solution of this is $h = 4\cdot8$. Thus a bore would have to be $4\cdot8$ feet high to travel into water 5 feet deep with the same velocity that a 2-foot bore travels in water 10 feet deep. If the bore enters a channel

with negligible initial depth, the height has to become 6·5 feet to travel
with the same velocity. Such considerations as these indicate that it is
to be expected that the wave of a bore will attain considerably greater
amplitude near the banks. In fact, near the banks, the bore takes the
form of a wave rather than a wall of water and the level behind it is
lower than the crest of the wave, as the photographs of the Mascaret
on the Seine clearly show. Indeed, in the case of the Mascaret the wave
in the centre of the river is barely perceptible. Taking the depth of the
Seine to be of the order of 25 feet, a bore of imperceptible amplitude
in mid-stream would travel at a speed of $\sqrt{25g}$ feet per second. Where
the depth of water was only 5 feet before its arrival, a bore, in order to
travel with this velocity, would have to have a height h given by

$$\frac{(5 + h)^2 g}{5 + \dfrac{h}{2}} = 25g$$

giving $\qquad\qquad\qquad h = 11\cdot3$ feet

If the depth were small before the arrival of the bore the height of
the wave would have to attain 12·5 feet. These heights are of the same
order of magnitude as those observed in the Mascaret along the banks
of the Seine at Caudebec-en-Caux. According to this simple theory
the height of a tidal bore along the banks of a river will depend upon
the depth of the river in the middle. The deeper the river, the higher
will be the wave along the banks, assuming that the water shelves
gradually. When a fast tide mounts a deep river like the lower Seine
it brings a very large mass of water upstream. The energy contained
in such a mass moving at 3 or 4 miles an hour is very large. The dissipation of this energy, even by large waves proceeding along the banks,
is a slow process and the tide is able to transfer sufficient energy to
the wave to carry it for long distances up the river—in the case of the
Seine, almost to Rouen. If the sides are vertical, of course, as may be
more nearly the case when works have been carried out to control the
river and wharves built on the banks, the depth of the river may
approximate to the same value all across its width. In such a case, of
course, there would be no increase in amplitude near the banks.

The theory so far discussed has not dealt with the question of the
formation of a tidal bore in a river. It has taken it as a *fait accompli*
and investigated the consequences of its appearance on the scene. It is
of interest to discuss also the question of the initiation of a bore. Why,
for example, does one occur in the Severn but not in the Thames?
Why does one form in the River Trent but not in any of the other
rivers which flow into the Humber?

It has been pointed out that as a travelling tidal wave enters shallow water its front steepens and its back flattens. The period of the tide, however, is some 12 hours and the wavelength of any tidal wave is necessarily very long. It is thus highly doubtful if this steepening of the front of a tidal wave could become sufficiently marked to produce a bore in a river. The causes of bores, with little doubt, are to be sought elsewhere.

It is not, however, an easy matter to devise a simple theory of the initiation of a tidal bore. The motion during the initial formation of a bore cannot be a steady one and Rayleigh's device of an adverse current is ineffective in transforming the problem into one of steady motion. All that can be done simply is to discuss the effects of the narrowing of the channel of a river or a rise in its bed upon the surface of a steady current of water flowing in it. This may give some indications pointing to the likely establishment of a bore, but cannot be made exact. However, the results have considerable interest in themselves and help to

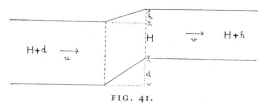

FIG. 41.

explain, for example, the nature of the undulations of the surface of a stream as it flows over an uneven bottom. We begin by investigating the effect on the surface of a rise in the bed of a stream.

Let us consider a stream flowing to the right with velocity u and suppose that it meets an incline in its bed of height d, as in Fig. 41. Let us further suppose that, as a result, the surface rises by an amount h. The motion will be steady and the question of the introduction of an adverse current does not arise in this case. The deformity of the surface will be stationary, being fixed in position by the rise in the bed of the stream.

As before, we make use of our two relations—that for the change in energy of a particle in the surface, on the one hand, and the equation of continuity, on the other. Suppose the velocity of the water, after having mounted the incline, is v. The energy equation gives us

$$\frac{mu^2}{2} - \frac{mv^2}{2} = mgh$$

i.e.
$$u^2 - v^2 = 2gh$$

or
$$(u - v)(u + v) = 2gh \qquad . \qquad . \qquad . \quad 12$$

The equation of continuity is

$$(H + d)u = (H + h)v$$

i.e.
$$\frac{v}{u} = \frac{H + d}{H + h} \qquad . \qquad . \qquad . \qquad . \quad 13$$

Adding 1 to each side we get

$$\frac{u + v}{u} = \frac{2H + h + d}{H + h}$$

Similarly by subtracting 1 from each side we get

$$\frac{v - u}{u} = \frac{d - h}{H + h}$$

therefore

$$(u + v)(u - v) = \frac{u^2(2H + h + d)(h - d)}{(H + h)^2}$$

which by Equation 12, gives us

$$\frac{u^2(2H + h + d)(h - d)}{(H + h)^2} = 2gh$$

therefore

$$(H + h)^2 2gh = u^2(2H + h + d)(h - d)$$

Multiplying this out we get

$$(H^2 + 2Hh + h^2)2gh = u^2h(2H + h + d) - u^2d(2H + h + d)$$

If we restrict ourselves to cases where h and d are small we may neglect squares and products of these quantities. To this order of accuracy we obtain

$$2H^2gh = u^2(2Hh - 2dH)$$

Collecting up the terms in h and dividing throughout by $2H$ we have

$$h(u^2 - gH) = u^2d$$

i.e.
$$h = \frac{u^2d}{u^2 - gH}$$

or dividing top and bottom on the right-hand side by u^2

$$h = \frac{d}{1 - \dfrac{gH}{u^2}} \qquad . \qquad . \qquad . \qquad . \quad 14$$

Let us consider first the case, which is the most common in practice, of a stream the velocity of which is less than $\sqrt{gH}$. In that case $\dfrac{gH}{u^2}$ is greater than 1 and the expression at the bottom of the right-hand side

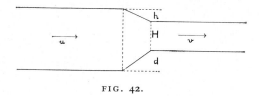

FIG. 42.

of Equation 14 is negative. If d is positive, therefore, which means that the bed of the stream rises as is drawn in Fig. 41, then the elevation, h, of the surface is negative. That is to say the surface of the water is depressed where the bed of the stream rises. Fig. 41 would, therefore, be incorrectly drawn for such a case. When the velocity of the stream is less than $\sqrt{gH}$, the figure should, in fact, be drawn as Fig. 42.

Had d been negative, that is to say had the bed of the stream become lower, the surface of the water would have risen. The surface of the water in a stream, the velocity of which is less than $\sqrt{gH}$, therefore, mirrors the elevations and depressions of the bottom but in reverse. The state of affairs is illustrated in Fig. 43. At first sight this result appears paradoxical. It is occasioned by the fact that when the bed of the stream rises, so that the water is less deep, the velocity of the water increases. A particle of water in the surface, therefore, must run downhill and not up, if it is to be speeded up.

When the velocity of the stream is very small, $\dfrac{gH}{u^2}$ is large, and the depression, h, of the surface is very small. As the speed of the stream increases the depression of the surface also increases. When the velocity of the stream reaches the critical value $\sqrt{gH}$, Equation 14 indicates that the depression of the surface becomes infinitely large. The theory, however, has been worked out on the assumption that the changes in elevation of bed and surface are small, so that Equation 14 will cease to be valid long before this happens. Equation 14 has been graphed in Fig. 44.

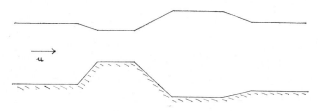

FIG. 43.—*Velocity of stream less than* $\sqrt{gH}$.

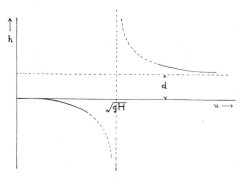

FIG. 44.

The portion of the curve near the value $u = \sqrt{gH}$ has been dotted to indicate that the relation holds, in practice, only when h and d are small. When the velocity of the stream exceeds the critical value $\sqrt{gH}$, the elevation of the surface becomes positive, and the water surface again mirrors the variations in the bed, but this time positively. For very large velocities the elevation of the surface tends to become equal to the elevation of the bed and the stream would flow with a constant cross-section. Such a state of affairs, corresponding to a velocity of a stream exceeding the critical value $\sqrt{gH}$, is illustrated in Fig. 45. In this case, however, the flow becomes a rushing, tumbling one, and the surface is no longer smooth, as indicated in the figure, which is drawn to simplify the situation.

Examples corresponding to Figs. 43 or 45 can be seen in mountain streams. The conditions of Fig. 43, with the surface mirroring the bed in reverse, are commonly to be seen.

It is tempting to discuss the formation of a tidal bore on the lines of Fig. 46, which depicts the tide entering a river with a sloping bed. As the tide flows over the inclined portion of the bed its level may be expected to fall, as drawn in the figure. Our discussion, however, has been based on the assumption of steady flow, and this would not be the case in Fig. 46, so that the results of the previous theory cannot be

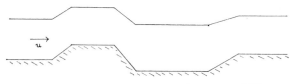

FIG. 45.—*Velocity of stream greater than* $\sqrt{gH}$.

applied directly. Nevertheless, if the change in the steady conditions takes place sufficiently slowly, an idea of the developments which would ensue may be gleaned. As the tidal current began to flow into the shallow section produced by the rise in the river bed, we would start with a fall in level, as just described. This drop in level would become steadily greater as the velocity of the tidal current increased. If the river were shallow enough, a point might be reached for the velocity, u, of the current, to exceed $\sqrt{gH}$. Should this happen, a sudden rise in the surface level of the water as it mounted the gradient of the bed, would replace the previous fall. A discontinuity would occur as the velocity passed through the critical value $\sqrt{gH}$ and a 'wall of water' constituting a bore could be produced, which would travel up the higher reaches, overtaking the lower water in front. It is a fall in the bed of the river as it flows into the Humber which distinguishes the Trent from the

FIG. 46.

other rivers which join the same estuary. The gradient of the bed of the river increases towards the point where it joins the Humber. The name 'Trent Falls', which appears on the Ordnance Survey maps, however, is misleading. It is merely the name of the confluence of the Trent and Humber—usually called an 'Outfall'. There is a strong current at the outfall which has been responsible for barge fatalities, but it is no doubt the gradient in the bed of the river, combined with sandbanks in the same area and a narrowing of the channel, which leads to the formation of the aegir on the Trent but not on the other rivers flowing into the Humber.

A similar first order theory, given in Appendix III, can be worked out to show the effect of a narrowing in the width of a river as the tide flows up it. Suppose the width of a river changes from B to $B - \beta$. Let the depth of water in the wide portion be H. Suppose the level in the narrow section to be h feet below the surface in the wide section. Then to the first order in h and β, the result of such a calculation is to show that

$$\frac{h}{\beta} = \frac{u^2}{gB\left(1 - \dfrac{u^2}{gH}\right)} \quad . \qquad . \qquad . \qquad . \quad 15$$

When the velocity u of the stream in the wide section is less than $\sqrt{gH}$, h is positive. That is to say, the state of affairs corresponds to Fig. 47, with the water level lower in the narrow section than in the wide. When the velocity of the stream in the wide section is greater than $\sqrt{gH}$, h becomes negative and the level of the surface in the narrow section is above that in the wide. The transition between the two states is sudden, just as it was in the case previously considered when the river became shallower.

In the formation of a bore we have to consider a gradual change in the steady conditions assumed in the theory. When the incoming tide begins to flow, the velocity of the current will be small and the level of the water surface will fall as the river narrows. This fall will increase as the velocity of the incoming tide increases. Should the velocity of the tidal current exceed $\sqrt{gH}$, a sudden change occurs in the distribution

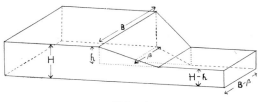

FIG. 47.

of levels, that in the narrow section rising above the level in the wider parts. Thus a sudden increase in the height of the water entering the narrow section will occur and a wall of water could again proceed up the narrow section. This would be the tidal bore. Thus conditions which would favour the formation of a bore in the narrowing estuary would be shallow water in the wide section, so that H is small enough for the tidal current to exceed a velocity of $\sqrt{gH}$ at the mouth of the narrower part.

Suppose we have a tidal stream travelling at 4 miles per hour, a not uncommon figure for the Severn and Trent, what must be the limit of the depth of water for the critical velocity to be exceeded? 4 miles per hour is approximately 6 feet per second, so that the depth H must be equal to or less than the value given by the relation

$$6 = \sqrt{32 . H}$$

This gives us

$$H = \frac{36}{32} \text{ feet}$$
$$= 1 \text{ foot } 1\tfrac{1}{2} \text{ inches}$$

With a tidal current of 6 miles per hour (i.e. 9 feet per second) the maximum depth for bore formation would be 2 feet 6 inches.

If this theory of the formation of a bore is to be applicable in particular cases, it is obvious that very shallow water indeed must occur at the mouths of the rivers concerned. One would look for sandbanks exposed or nearly exposed at low tide, over which strong tidal currents can flow. On this theory it would be conditions at low water, or soon after low water when the returning tide had started to flow strongly, which would determine whether a bore would form or not. At neap tides low water might not be low enough for the critical velocity to be exceeded. The occurrence of a bore would depend not so much upon the height of high tide at springs as on the position of low water.

A question which may have occurred to the reader is, if bores are formed by an incoming tide, why does one not form as the water drains away as the tide recedes? If the draining away were a sudden process one would expect a wave to spread up the river as the 'negative bore' described in the next chapter. One reason is that the velocity of the receding tide is much less than that of the advancing tide. A second reason can now be seen to be that the depths are very much greater as the tide ebbs than they were when it commenced to come in, and the conditions of bore formation would not develop.

These conditions of shallow water at low tide obtain in the Severn where there are extensive sandbanks just below the reaches where the bore forms. In particular there are the Noose and Frampton Sands and it is known that the position and extent of these banks have considerable influence on the formation of the bore in that river. Extensive sandbanks also occur in the lower reaches of the River Kent, in Westmorland, on which bores also form at spring tides. Sand and mudbanks are again present off the mouth of the Parrett and in its lower reaches, and this is another river in which tidal bores form on spring tides.

In his report on the bore on the Chien Tang Kiang in 1888 Admiral Usborne Moore comments on the strength of the tidal currents crossing the sandbanks at the mouth of the river. His remarks are of particular interest in this connection since he worked on a theory of bore formation which was different from that just explained. He referred it to the 'conflict' between the incoming tide and the outflow of the river. His account of the strength of the tidal currents over the sandbanks is thus unlikely to have been influenced by any preconceived ideas about what must happen. 'Of course', he wrote, 'one does not visit an estuary of the shape of Hang Chau Gulf without anticipating very strong tides and preparing for them; but it was entirely contrary to our previous experience to find these 8 to 11-knot streams running over sand only just covered with water. I imagined they were confined to the channels.

. . . The 10-knot rush comes when there is 1 to 2 feet of water over the sand flats.' Later he speaks of 'water banking up into the small end of the funnel running downhill, and having in front a vast field of sand, the greater portion of which is dry when this force is set in motion, and indeed for some minutes afterwards. Presently the water begins to set over the flats slowly. . . . When 2 feet of the sand is covered the flood stream runs with great impetuosity.' The water is 'precipitated over the vast bar of sand into the Chien Tang'. Here it enters the comparatively narrow channel of the river, though it is still nearly a mile wide at this point at low water. The critical velocity is clearly exceeded and the most spectacular of bores to be recorded is formed. 'The regularity of its appearance and shape, the distance at which it is heard at night and seen by day; its charge against the sea wall; its speed, height, gleaming front and thundering roar as it tears past the observer, render it a most impressive phenomenon.'

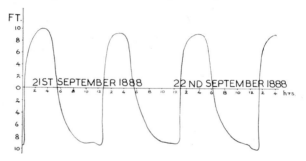

FIG. 48.—*Tidal curve for Haining from readings of Admiral Usborne Moore.*

APPENDIX II

In Chapter V the velocity of a tidal bore ascending a river was calculated, making the assumption that the particle velocity in the current following the bore was small compared with the velocity of the bore itself. This assumption will provide only a roughly approximate solution. It is equivalent to the assumption that the amplitude of the bore is infinitesimally small. In the case of the bore on the Severn, the tidal current after the bore has passed commonly has a speed of just under 4 miles per hour while the bore itself travels at about 12 miles per hour. The formula of Chapter V, therefore, has been calculated neglecting quantities of the order of 10 per cent. It is little more laborious to retain the second order term which was neglected in the text.

Using the figures and symbols of Chapter V we have the equation of continuity (Equation 7) as before

$$hc = u(H + h) \qquad . \qquad . \qquad . \qquad \text{AII 1}$$

We have also the energy relation (Equation 8)

$$cu - \frac{u^2}{2} = gh \qquad . \qquad . \qquad . \qquad \text{AII 2}$$

Substituting the value of $u = \dfrac{hc}{H + h}$ from Equation AII 1, we have

$$\frac{c^2h}{H + h} - \frac{c^2h^2}{2(H + h)^2} = gh$$

Therefore

$$\frac{c^2h(2H + h)}{2(H + h)^2} = gh$$

giving

$$c^2 = \frac{2(H + h)^2 g}{2H + h}$$

or

$$c = \sqrt{\frac{(H + h)^2 g}{H + \dfrac{h}{2}}} \qquad . \qquad . \qquad \text{AII 3}$$

If the expression under the square root is expanded to the first order in h it gives

$$c = \sqrt{H\left(1 + \frac{2h}{H} - \frac{h}{2H}\right)}$$

$$= \sqrt{\left(H + \frac{3h}{2}\right)g}$$

APPENDIX III

The Change in River Level caused by a Narrowing of the Channel

Consider a stream entering a narrower part of the channel. Suppose the level of the water in the narrow section to be at a distance h below that in the wide section and let β be the decrease in width, as in Fig. 49.

The equation of continuity gives

$$BHu = (H - h)(B - \beta)v$$

Therefore

$$\frac{v}{u} = \frac{BH}{(H - h)(B - \beta)}$$

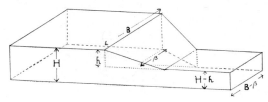

FIG. 49.

Therefore
$$\frac{v + u}{u} = \frac{2BH - \beta H - Bh}{(H - h)(B - \beta)}$$

to the first order in h and β, and

$$\frac{v - u}{u} = \frac{\beta H + Bh}{(H - h)(B - \beta)}$$

whence
$$v^2 - u^2 = \frac{u^2(2BH - \beta H - Bh)(\beta H + Bh)}{(H - h)^2(B - \beta)^2}$$

The energy relation gives
$$v^2 - u^2 = 2gh$$

Therefore, retaining only first order terms in h and β

$$u^2(2BH^2\beta + 2B^2Hh) = 2gh(H^2 - 2Hh)(B^2 - 2B\beta)$$
$$= 2gh(H^2B^2 + \text{terms in } h \text{ and } \beta)$$
$$= 2ghH^2B^2$$

Therefore, collecting up terms in h

$$h(gH^2B^2 - u^2B^2H) = u^2B\beta H^2$$

which gives

$$\frac{h}{\beta} = \frac{u^2BH^2}{gH^2B^2 - u^2B^2H} = \frac{u^2}{gB\left(1 - \dfrac{u^2}{gH}\right)}$$

When u is less than $\sqrt{gh}$, h is positive and the surface is depressed in the narrower section.

When u is greater than $\sqrt{gH}$, h is negative and the surface is elevated in the narrower section.

PLATE IX.—*A plunging breaker.*

CHAPTER VI

The Theory of Gravity Waves in Shallow Water

IN shallow water motion in a vertical direction is restricted so that the predominant movement is backwards and forwards. It thus has a degree of similarity with the movement of water in a tidal bore, which is also predominantly horizontal, although elevations and depressions occur in the surface. A small extension of the theory of the tidal bore already studied will furnish an explanation of the properties of waves in shallow water.

According to the theory of the tidal bore of Chapter V, the velocity of propagation is given to a first approximation by the expression $c = \sqrt{g(H + h)}$.

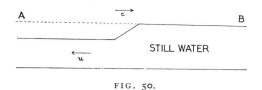

FIG. 50.

Here $H + h$ is the depth of water after the bore has passed. It is the depth of the tidal stream travelling forwards. To develop from this a theory of waves let us consider the case of what might be termed a 'negative bore'.

Suppose we have a canal filled to the level AB with still water (Fig. 50) and suppose further that a lockgate collapses to the left of A so that water starts to flow away. A wave separating moving water to the left from still water to the right will move along the canal with some velocity which we will call c. The water in the canal will remain unaffected until the arrival of the wave and after its passage will move to the left with velocity, say, u feet per second. Let us determine the velocity of propagation, c, of the wave.

As in the previous discussions we need to reduce the problem to one of steady flow and this we can do by Rayleigh's method of the adverse current. Instead of considering initially still water in a canal, let us imagine a long tank travelling to the left with the wave velocity c, thus bringing the wave to rest. The previously still water now approaches the wave with velocity c. Water particles on the surface

slide down the slope of the wave and are carried away with velocity
$c + u$. This state of affairs is represented in Fig. 51.

Suppose the depth of the undisturbed water to the right of the wave
is H, and let the height of the wave through which the water descends
be h. As before, we employ the two conditions of continuity and of
energy to determine the velocity of the wave.

Applying the condition of continuity and considering a section of
the water 1 foot wide, we see that water arrives at the section LM at

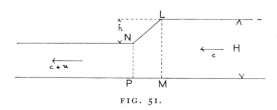

FIG. 51.

the rate Hc cubic feet per second. It leaves NP at the rate $(H - h)(c + u)$.
Under steady conditions as much water must leave per second from
NP as arrives at LM. Therefore

$$Hc = (H - h)(c + u)$$
$$= Hc + Hu - hc - hu$$

giving us

$$u(H - h) = hc \qquad . \qquad . \qquad . \qquad . \qquad 16$$

A particle of water in the surface, of mass m, arrives at L with the
kinetic energy $\dfrac{mc^2}{2}$. It leaves from N with a kinetic energy $\dfrac{m(c + u)^2}{2}$.
The difference must have been provided by the work done by gravity
on the particle in descending the height h, as it slid down the wave.

Therefore

$$\frac{m(c + u)^2}{2} - \frac{mc^2}{2} = mgh$$

or

$$c^2 + 2uc + u^2 - c^2 = 2gh$$

or

$$2uc + u^2 = 2gh \qquad . \qquad . \qquad . \qquad . \qquad 17$$

As before, let us ease the calculation by neglecting squares of the
particle velocity, which will be small compared with the velocity of
the wave, reserving the more complete calculation for Appendix IV.
We shall then have

$$uc = gh \qquad . \qquad . \qquad . \qquad . \qquad 18$$

Equation 16 gives us

$$u = \frac{hc}{H - h}$$

and substituting this value into Equation 18 we obtain

$$\frac{hc^2}{H - h} = gh$$

from which it follows that

$$c = \sqrt{g(H - h)} \qquad . \qquad . \qquad . \qquad . \qquad 19$$

The velocity of propagation of the wave is thus determined by the depth of water in the shallow section. In both cases, of the positive and negative bores, the velocity of propagation depends upon the depth of water in the section of the river where movement is taking place. In the normal or positive bore this is in the deeper water behind the advancing wave. In the case of a negative bore it is in the shallower water but again behind the advancing wave.

These results follow from the assumption that the particle velocity of the water is small compared with the velocity of propagation of the wave, which is only roughly true. The more accurate calculations in which this assumption is not made are given in Appendices II and IV. There it is shown that to the first order in the height of the wave, the velocity of a positive bore is given by the expression

$$c = \sqrt{g\left(H + \frac{3h}{2}\right)}$$

while the corresponding equation for a negative bore is

$$c = \sqrt{g\left(H - \frac{3h}{2}\right)}$$

If we write the velocity of propagation as $c = \sqrt{gD}$, where D is the depth, we see that a positive bore is propagated with a velocity corresponding to a depth equal to that of the deeper water behind the wave, increased by one half the height of the wave, whereas a negative bore is propagated with a velocity corresponding to a depth of water equal to that in the shallow water behind the wave decreased by one half the height of the wave. Thus for the same undisturbed depth of water in a stream a positive bore will travel more quickly than a negative one.

We are now in a position to construct a picture of a solitary wave in shallow water. For simplicity let us consider first a wave of which the height is small compared with the depth of the water, so that the effect of differences of depth under the wave on its velocity of propagation may be neglected. Let us start a positive bore moving up a trough by means of a movable piston and then stop the motion of the piston after it has travelled a short distance. The water in front of the piston returns to its former level and a wave is propagated up the trough.

This wave may be looked upon as a positive bore moving up the trough followed by an equal and opposite negative one which restores the water to its original position after the passage of the wave. The conditions created are depicted in Fig. 52.

A section of water in the trough bounded by the planes AB and CD will be moving forward under the wave. In front and behind will be still water. The wave will travel forwards with a velocity c which will be greater than that of the particles between AB and CD. The forward motion will, therefore, constantly be being transferred to particles in front, and the particles under the wave will drop behind it as the latter is propagated forwards. Their velocity will diminish and they will come to rest. As the wave passes over a section of the water, the particles of which it is composed will move forward a certain distance and then resume their state of rest. As the wave passes along the trough the whole body of the water in it will be given a displacement to the right.

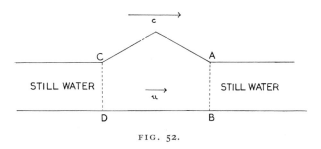

FIG. 52.

This will go on until the wave reaches the end of the trough, when what happens will depend upon how the end is arranged. For the moment we may suppose that the trough is connected to a very large tank into which the wave will pass, so that the extra water which passes with it will not affect appreciably the level of the water in the tank.

In waves, as we know them, on the sea, we do not have any large-scale transport of water forwards as the waves pass. Waves travel past objects in the sea leaving them more or less in the same position. We do not have waves, furthermore, which have only peaks rising above the undisturbed level of the water. Waves on the sea have troughs below the undisturbed sea level as well. To complete our picture, therefore, we would have to move our piston in the trough back to its original position, and this would be enough to produce a negative bore sufficient to give a trough following the crest of the positive bore.

The new state of affairs is illustrated in Fig. 53. Between the planes AB and DC the water moves forward as before. Between DC and EF

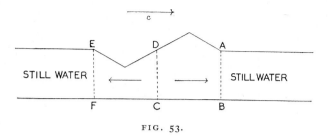

FIG. 53.

it moves backwards as with a negative bore followed by a compensating positive one.

To make the picture correspond to the formation of a train of waves the movement of the piston would have to be continuous, backwards and forwards. The waves will then extend through the whole trough and there will be no still water either in front of or behind them. The complete picture is sketched in Fig. 54. Waves follow each other at regular intervals. Under the crests the water moves forward, in the same direction as the waves are being propagated, whilst under the troughs it moves backwards in the opposite direction.

If D is the mean depth the velocity of propagation will be

$$c = \sqrt{gD}$$

so long as the amplitude of the wave is small enough so that variations in depth can be neglected.

It will be noted that in shallow water the wave motion is predominantly horizontal and extends right to the bed of the sea. Sections of the water under the crest move forward bodily with the wave and corresponding complete sections under the troughs move in the opposite direction. This simple picture will describe the phenomena only when two conditions are fulfilled. One is that the water is shallow. This will be the case when the depth is small compared with the wavelength of the waves. The second is that the height of the waves is small compared with the depth. In deep water the motion is quite different—vertical

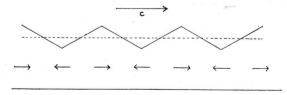

FIG. 54.

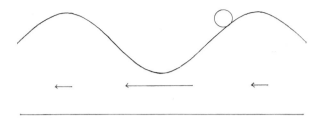

FIG. 55.

motion is as important as horizontal and the movement of the water does not extend to the bed of the sea. The conditions so far postulated, therefore, will apply in a limited region near the shore only.

This arrangement of forward movement under the crests and backward motion under the troughs can be approached very simply by means of a model. When considering Lord Rayleigh's device of the adverse current to obtain steady flow in the case of wave motion, it was concluded that when the waves are thus rendered stationary, particles in the surface flow over the waves as a perfectly smooth particle would slide over a perfectly smooth curve. In the model indicated diagrammatically in Fig. 55, a switchback has been cut out of plywood in the form of the waves. These are held stationary to represent waves subjected to a Rayleigh adverse current. Two such pieces of plywood, separated by distance pieces, will form a railway over which a ball-bearing or billiard ball may be rolled. A photograph of the model is reproduced in Plate 9. The motion of the ball over the switchback will simulate the movement of a particle sliding over a smooth curve.

PLATE 9.—*A billiard ball rolling over a switchback in the form of a wave, to represent the motion of water particles in waves held stationary by an adverse current.*

The ball will, in fact, travel in the direction of the adverse current (from right to left in the figure), and, in turn, will simulate the motion of the water particles over the waves held stationary by the adverse current. Plate 10 is a photograph of successive positions of the ball as it rolls over the switchback of the waves. It was taken by means of an 8-mm ciné camera running at 64 frames per second (to secure as good definition as possible). Every fourth picture was then projected on to a translucent screen and photographed one after the other on to the same plate in a still camera, thus producing a composite picture. Such pictures can also be taken by means of an electronic flash stroboscope,

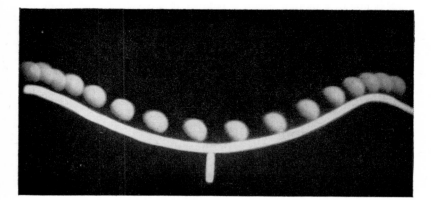

PLATE 10.—*Composite photograph of successive positions of a billiard ball rolling over a stationary wave. Taken by means of an 8-mm ciné camera, at 64 frames per second, every fourth frame being projected and rephotographed on to the same plate in a still camera.*

which is a comparatively expensive piece of equipment, or very simply by photographing the moving ball in a still camera with a revolving disc in front of the lens. Slots are cut in the disc to make the successive exposures. The definition obtained with the rotating shutter is not as good as with the other methods but it is often good enough for experimental purposes.

As the ball-bearing is rolled over the switchback it will be obvious that it will travel at high speed in the troughs and pass over the crests at a lower speed. This is shown clearly in the photograph of Plate 9 which depicts the position of the ball at the ends of equal intervals of time. On the crests the positions are close together and they are spaced out farther apart in the troughs. Let us now remove the adverse

PLATE 12.—*Wave of larger amplitude in the wave tank.*

current which holds the waves stationary and allow them to travel towards the right. The velocity of the adverse current will be such that when it is removed the ball merely moves through a limited distance only and does not travel, on the whole, to the right or the left. The velocity of the adverse current must therefore lie between the speed of the ball as it passes the crests and its speed passing through the

PLATE 13.—*Wave of large amplitude in the wave tank. The leading slope on the right is steeper than that on the left.*

Substituting the value for $c^2 = (H + h)g$ (from Equation 10), we obtain for u^2

$$u^2 = \frac{h^2 g}{H + h} \qquad . \qquad . \qquad . \qquad . \qquad 20$$

This will be the expression for the velocity of the water particles in the surface of a crest of height h.

Similarly for a trough the equation of continuity, as in the negative bore, will be

$$u(H - h) = ch$$

PLATE 14.—*Wave in a large tank in an experimental research station. The leading edge is on the left and is steeper than the following slope.*

which gives
$$u^2 = \frac{c^2 h^2}{(H-h)^2}$$

Again substituting the value for $c^2 = (H-h)g$ for a trough (from Equation 19), we obtain

$$u^2 = \frac{h^2 g}{(H-h)} \qquad . \qquad . \qquad . \qquad . \qquad 21$$

Thus we see that the velocity of the water particles on the surface of a crest $\left(u = \sqrt{\dfrac{h^2 g}{H+h}}\right)$ is less than the velocity of the water on the surface of a trough $\left(u = \sqrt{\dfrac{h^2 g}{H-h}}\right)$. When the waves are advancing towards the shore, the velocity in the crest carries the particles shorewards and that in the trough seawards. It would appear at first sight, therefore, that waves should cause a drift of the surface water seawards. This would be contrary to experience, since casual observation indicates that floating objects are not carried rapidly shorewards or seawards, and that since flotsam is slowly cast up on the beach, what drift there is

FIG. 57.

of the surface waters must be towards the shore and not out to sea. Our conclusions from Equations 20 and 21, however, are not justified. In a crest the water particles are travelling with the waves, whereas in a trough they are travelling against them. Thus, if crests and troughs are equal, a particle will spend longer in the crests than in the troughs and what it gains in speed seaward in the troughs is counterbalanced by the longer time it has in the crests.

Our simple picture of waves with plane sides and equal crests and troughs is not worth pushing much further, since in practice waves do not possess this simple shape. We shall see when we come to discuss trochoidal waves that peaks tend to be short and high while troughs are long and shallow. Waves are much more like the trochoidal form shown in Fig. 57. To apply to such waves our simple considerations would need modification.

It is, however, worthwhile making an estimate of when one of our simple type of waves with equal crests and troughs would start to break. It cannot be long delayed after the velocity of the water particles on the surface of the crest equals the velocity of propagation of the trough in front of it. As this velocity is exceeded the particles would slide or fall down into the trough.

Equation 20 gives for the velocity u of the particles on the crest the expression

$$u^2 = \frac{h^2 g}{H + h}$$

the velocity of propagation of the trough, c, is given by

$$c^2 = (H - h)g$$

equating u and c gives

$$\frac{h^2}{H + h} = H - h$$

i.e., $h^2 = H^2 - h^2$

or $h^2 = \dfrac{H^2}{2}$

or $h = \dfrac{H}{\sqrt{2}} = \dfrac{H}{1 \cdot 4}$

A more complicated calculation shows that waves break when $h = \dfrac{H}{1 \cdot 28}$, which is not greatly different from the result given by the simple considerations above. We would thus expect waves to break when their height is about two-thirds the depth of the water above the undisturbed level.

The waves which we have been thinking about so far would take the form of long parallel ridges travelling over the sea in a direction at right angles to their length. The position of a wave at any subsequent time is simply the position it would occupy if each section of it advanced uniformly forward with the velocity appropriate to the depth. Waves, however, are not always straight and their velocity of propagation does not always remain constant because of variations in the depth. How may the subsequent position occupied by a wave be determined?

There is a well-known construction, given by the Dutch physicist Christian Huyghens in 1690, in his Traité de la Lumière, of which we shall need to avail ourselves later and which may not inappropriately be discussed here. Huyghens considered each point on a wave front as the source of a disturbance sending out circular wavelets with the velocity appropriate to the place where it is situated, as in Fig. 58a. The position of the wavefront at a subsequent time was obtained by considering the resultant effect arising from all the points on the original front. Thus, if we start with the wavefront HJ (Fig. 58b), it will be seen that the crests of all the wavelets tend to coincide, and thus

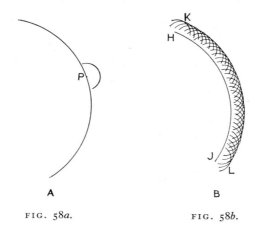

FIG. 58a.   FIG. 58b.

reinforce each other, along the line *KL*. At other places crests and troughs fall without system so that a crest is as likely to fall on a trough as on a crest. There is no reinforcement. *KL*, where all the wavelets reinforce, is thus the new position of the wavefront. The wavefront at a subsequent time is therefore the envelope of secondary wavelets spreading out from each point of the wave.

When the velocity varies from point to point the construction can only be carried out over small distances at a time, over which the velocity of propagation may be treated as uniform. The construction has then to be repeated again and again to follow the wavefront as it is propagated forwards under such conditions.

APPENDIX IV

Velocity of Propagation of a Negative Bore

The purpose of this Appendix is to deduce an expression for the velocity of propagation of the wave separating the moving from the still water, in the negative bore, without neglecting squares of the particle velocity *u*.

The two equations we have to solve are Equations 16 and 17. These are

$$u(H - h) = hc \qquad . \qquad . \qquad . \qquad \text{A IV 1}$$

$$2uc + u^2 = 2gh \qquad . \qquad . \qquad . \qquad \text{A IV 2}$$

Substituting $u = \dfrac{hc}{H - h}$ in Equation 17a we have

$$\frac{2hc^2}{H - h} + \frac{h^2c^2}{(H - h)^2} = 2gh$$

which gives

$$2hc^2(H - h) + h^2c^2 = 2gh(H - h)^2$$

i.e. $\qquad\qquad 2Hhc^2 - h^2c^2 = 2gh(H - h)^2$

i.e. $\qquad\qquad 2Hc^2 - hc^2 = 2g(H - h)^2$

i.e. $\qquad\qquad c^2 = \dfrac{2g(H - h)^2}{2H - h}$

$$= \frac{g(H - h)^2}{H - \dfrac{h}{2}}$$

We may compare this expression with the corresponding one for the normal (i.e. positive) bore

$$c^2 = \frac{g(H + h)^2}{H + \dfrac{h}{2}} \qquad . \qquad . \qquad . \quad \text{A IV 3}$$

Expanding this to the first order in h we obtain for the positive bore

$$c^2 = H\left(1 + \frac{2h}{H}\right)\left(1 - \frac{h}{H}\right)$$

i.e. $\qquad\qquad c^2 = g\left(H + \dfrac{3h}{2}\right) \qquad . \qquad . \qquad . \quad \text{A IV 4}$

while for the negative bore the corresponding expansion is

$$c^2 = H\left(1 - \frac{2h}{H}\right)\left(1 + \frac{h}{H}\right)$$

i.e. $\qquad\qquad c^2 = g\left(H - \dfrac{3h}{2}\right) \qquad . \qquad . \qquad . \quad \text{A IV 5}$

If we express both formulae as $c = \sqrt{gD}$, where D is the depth, we find that the positive bore travels with a velocity corresponding to the depth of the deep water side increased by half the height of the wave, whereas the negative bore travels with a velocity corresponding to the depth of the shallow water side decreased by half the height of the wave.

CHAPTER VII

Waves as seen from the Shore; the Properties of Waves in Shallow Water

S I M P L E theoretical considerations like those of Chapter VI and experiments in wave tanks or tubes, such as those described in Chapter V, have led us to the equation for the velocity of waves in shallow water.

$$c = \sqrt{gD}$$

where D is the depth and g the acceleration of gravity. These two approaches are mutually supporting and it is well to have both of them to furnish confidence in the result. The non-mathematical reader, however, may be content to rely on the experimental evidence as the basis for his acceptance of this relation. We have already met occasions in connection with the formation of tidal bores which have illustrated the extraordinary and ubiquitous importance which this relation possesses. It is the basis for the explanation of very many of the properties of waves in rivers and near the seashore, and crops up in unexpected places such as the discharge of water over weirs, and in the wakes produced by vessels.

One particular application of it was discovered, no doubt inadvertently, by a horse! The discovery was made on the Glasgow and Ardrossan Canal. It was described in a paper read to the Royal Society of Edinburgh on April 4th 1837 by John Scott Russell, M.A., and published in the transactions of the Society in 1840. It is quoted *in extenso* by Lord Kelvin in a paper in the *Philosophical Magazine*, Volume XXII, in October 1886, from which the following is taken.

'Canal navigation furnishes at once the most interesting illustrations of the interference of the wave, and most important opportunities for the application of its principles to an improved system of practice. It is to the diminished anterior section of displacement, produced by raising a vessel with a sudden impulse to the summit of the progressive wave, that a very great improvement, recently introduced into canal transport, owes its existence. As far as I am able to learn the isolated fact was discovered accidentally on the Glasgow and Ardrossan Canal of small dimensions. A spirited horse in the boat of William Houston, Esq., one of the proprietors of the Works, took fright and ran off, dragging the boat with it, and it was then observed, to Mr Houston's astonishment, that the foaming stern surge which used to devastate the banks ceased and the vessel was carried on through water comparatively smooth, with a resistance very greatly diminished. Mr Houston had the tact to perceive the mercantile value of this fact to the Canal Company with which he was connected and devoted himself to introducing on that Canal vessels moving with this high velocity. The result of this improvement was so valuable in a mercantile point of view, as to bring, from the conveyance of passengers at high velocity, a large increase of revenue to the Canal Proprietors. Passengers and luggage are conveyed in light boats, about 60 feet long and 6 feet wide, made of thin sheet iron and drawn by a pair of horses. The boat starts at a slow velocity behind the wave and at a given signal it is by a sudden jerk of the horses drawn up on the top of the wave, where it moves with diminished resistance, at the rate of 7, 8 or 9 miles an hour.'

The resistance to a boat moving through the water is due in large part to the generation of waves, which travel along with it, and to the maintenance of this system of waves goes a large fraction of the energy required to drive the boat forward. These waves develop to the rear of the boat and tail along behind it carrying the boat's energy with them and dissipating it by friction with the banks and the bottom. Lord Kelvin remarks, 'the "diminished anterior section of displacement produced by raising a vessel with a sudden impulse to the summit of the progressive wave" is no doubt a correct observation of an essential feature of the phenomenon; but it is the annulment of "the foaming stern surge which (at the lower speeds) used to devastate the banks" that gives the direct explanation of the diminished resistance. It is, in fact, easy to see that when the motion is steady, no waves can be left astern of a boat towed through a canal at a speed greater than $\sqrt{gD}$, the velocity of an infinitely long wave in the canal.' This system of canal boat operation became known as the Scottish 'Fly-boat' method and was worked on the Forth and Clyde Canal between Edinburgh and Glasgow as well as on the Glasgow and Ardrossan Canal.

The modern speed boat operates on the same principle, at least in shallow water, so far as we have seen at the moment. There used also to be a method of rowing a Naval whaler in races which may have been inspired by the same phenomenon. I do not know if it is still practised. The method consisted in using the oars in an attempt to lift the boat out of the water at each stroke. It is not likely to be successful for the same reason as that pointed out by Lord Kelvin. It is the system of waves developed by the motion of the boat, 'the foaming stern surge' which dissipates the bulk of the energy supplied, and it is unlikely that a heavy whaler could be propelled manually at velocities exceeding $\sqrt{gD}$, however much it was lifted by the strokes of the oars.

What is the effect of sea waves on the motion of a boat being rowed across a rough sea? We have seen that actual transport of material at

PLATE X.—*The River Dee, showing the deposition of gravel on the inner sides of the river's meanders.*

the surface of the water by waves is at least very slow indeed and unlikely to affect the speed of a rowing boat, and yet the feeling is certainly obtained that more rapid progress is made travelling with the waves than against them. Is there any foundation for this feeling or is it a purely psychological impression? The water moves forward with the waves in the crests and backwards against their direction of propagation, in the troughs. It might seem that what is gained on the crests would be lost in the troughs and that it would make no difference either way. When a boat is rowed with the waves, the latter, travelling faster, overtake it. This is, of course, true of both crest and trough. When the boat is on a crest, however, the water itself is travelling forwards in the same direction as the boat. The velocity of the water is added to that of the boat, which is thus able to stay longer on the crest, where the movement of the water is favourable, than it would have done had the water not been moving forward in this position. In the trough the reverse happens. The water moves in the opposite direction to the boat, which is therefore slowed down. The trough, therefore, passes by the boat more quickly than it would have done had the water been stationary. The boat thus spends a longer time on the crests and a shorter time in the troughs than it would have done had it not been propelled through the water but had simply floated on the surface. Had it simply floated on the surface it would not have been carried either forwards or backwards, on the whole, by a series of waves. By remaining longer on the crests where the movement of the water is favourable and spending less time in the troughs, where it is unfavourable, the boat is helped forward by the waves. Had the boat been rowed faster than the waves, this would no longer have been true, since the forward velocity of the water in the crests would have helped the boat pass through the crests more quickly, whereas the opposing velocity in the troughs would have caused it to overtake them more slowly and thus spend a longer time under adverse conditions. Rowing against the waves the slow boat will, of course, be impeded, since it will pass through the troughs, where the velocity of the water is favourable, more quickly, and be retarded on the crests and thus spend longer on them in unfavourable conditions. This is also true of a faster boat which would be impeded in the same way. The faster boat, in fact, is impeded whether it is travelling with or against the waves. It is only the slower boat, being overtaken by the waves, which is helped when travelling in the same direction as they are being propagated.

As has already been remarked, although the movement of the surface of the water is backwards and forwards during the passage of waves, and there is virtually no resultant transport of material, nevertheless floatsam does, in fact, get cast up on the shore eventually. There must

G

therefore be a very slow surface current shorewards. A corresponding seaward current must, in consequence, exist lower down since water does not accumulate on the shore. Both theory and observation indicate that this is so.

Theories differ, however, according to where the reverse current is situated. Assuming non-rotational motion Stokes calculated a velocity profile as in Fig. 59. In practice waves are not strictly non-rotational. Experimentally Bagnold found strong forward velocities near the bottom and weaker backward velocities at the surface—the opposite, in fact, to what Stokes predicted. Other observers find forward motion in the surface and along the bottom with reversed motion in between. Longuet-Higgins has calculated that this variability is connected with

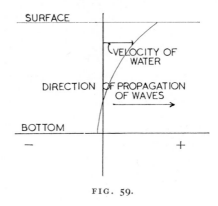

FIG. 59.

the slow diffusion of vorticity as the waves become established, the observed results depending upon the time for which the waves have been running in the experimental apparatus.

The velocity of these currents, however, is very small. This raises the vexed question of 'undertow'. The low velocity of the returning current near the bottom has led many to doubt the existence of undertow completely. The returning current would not attain a speed which could seriously inconvenience even a very moderate swimmer and, moreover, it flows along the sea-bed whereas the swimmer, or so one would hope, is in the surface layer where the flow is in the opposite direction. There are at least four possible contributory factors to the belief in undertow. The first is very obvious, a person swimming in a rough sea is out of his depth when on the crest of a wave and thus when he wishes to come ashore he naturally puts his feet down to stand on the bottom when he is in a trough. The water is then moving outwards away from the shore, the waves being propagated towards the shore.

The swimmer is also then lower in the water and he may obtain the feeling that the lower layers of the water are moving outwards rapidly. The second factor is as follows; when large waves break upon a beach considerable masses of water are cast up and these have to find their way back again to the sea. When the waves are high these return currents can be very rapid, and sufficient to bowl the unwary off their feet. The strength of the return currents can make bathing dangerous when the sea is rough and the waves are of long wavelength, so that each wave casts vast quantities of water on to the shore. The Atlantic rollers striking the north Cornish coast can produce conditions of this kind. A third factor may be one which has some similarity to the first. The height of waves varies, high ones being succeeded by low ones in cycles. The breaking of a group of high waves on the shore casts up much water, which finds its way back again to the sea when the succeeding group of smaller waves follows on. Our swimmer, desirous of coming ashore again, naturally chooses the quiet period in which to get out. This is precisely the time when the return current is liable to be at its maximum. The fourth factor is that known as the rip current. Because of unevenness in the sea-bed or of the presence of breakwaters, rocks or cliffs, waves sometimes tend to concentrate upon certain stretches of the beach. On these stretches water is cast up which finds its way back at neighbouring points where the waves are less vigorous, and the currents to which this gives rise are what are called rip currents. These frequently carve channels in the sand and, on occasion, may run at a speed of 2 knots. They are not of great extent laterally and if a swimmer realizes that he is caught in one he can get out of it by swimming parallel to the shore for a short distance. In water and faced with difficulty it is not, however, quite so simple to come to a decision about what is happening as it is when comfortably contemplating the situation by the fireside!

One thing, however, seems clear. Whatever may be meant by the term undertow, the return current along the sea-bed, corresponding to the slow shoreward drift of the surface water produced by waves, is not a phenomenon fraught with much danger. The other factors listed above, however, all have a measure of importance, and can give rise to difficulties for the unwary when conditions are not very severe and for all when they are.

Erosion of the coastline is a conspicuous effect of the pounding produced by waves and each year winter storms leave a record of fresh damage. Enormous masses of rock can be shifted by the sea and blocks of concrete weighing many tons in breakwaters thrown from their proper positions. Stones of all sizes are cast high on the beaches. What is the mechanism by which the sea is able to achieve this destruction?

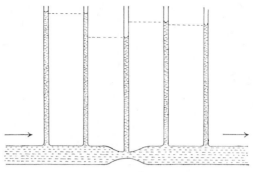

FIG. 60.

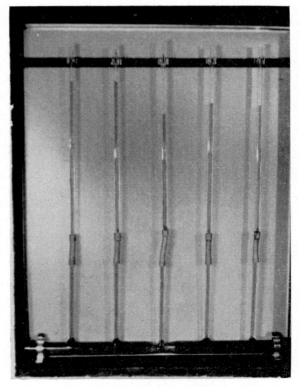

PLATE 15.—*Fall of pressure in a tube along which water flows. The side tubes indicate the pressure in the horizontal tube at the bottom. In the middle of the horizontal tube is a constriction and at this point the pressure is lowest.*

A very important factor which contributes to this ability of the sea to move heavy obstacles is simply buoyancy. The density of rock runs from about 2 to 3 grams per cubic centimetre. Immersed in water, therefore, rocks and stones lose from a third to a half of their weight and they are much more easy to move in water than in air.

A second factor is also involved in the movement of stones and shingle by the sea. It is the phenomenon known as the Bernoulli effect, after its discoverer Daniel Bernoulli (1700–82), a member of the family which produced as many mathematicians as the family of Bach did musicians. Daniel Bernoulli's particular work was the systematization of the theory of hydrodynamics. Bernoulli was the first to point out that the pressure in a liquid is, *ceteris paribus*, lowest where the liquid is moving fastest. This fact, though obvious on a moment's thought, leads to a number of apparently paradoxical results. It is obvious that if a slow-moving particle of liquid is to be accelerated it must move from the region of higher to one of lower pressure, and if it is to be slowed

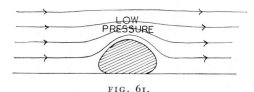

FIG. 61.

up again after being accelerated, it must go to a region of higher pressure. Pressure will, therefore, be lowest where the liquid moves fastest. Thus, if we make a tube with a constriction in it and connect side tubes to it to measure the pressure as water flows along it, as in Fig. 60, we find that the pressure falls at the narrow section and is higher on both sides. A photograph of such an apparatus in action is shown in Plate 15.

Water flowing over an obstacle is forced to move faster since the streamlines are constricted, as indicated in Fig. 61. The pressure above the obstacle is, therefore, reduced and the reduction in pressure may be sufficient to lift it. In a similar way very strong winds blowing over a house may lift off tiles, or in extreme cases such as a hurricane, even the whole roof, because of this effect.

Once the obstacle is lifted, still a third factor comes into operation, since when a liquid flows over an obstacle the streamlines are not smooth curves, as in Fig. 61, except on the upstream side, unless the velocity of the stream is very small. On the downstream side an eddy forms, as in Fig. 62. There is an upcurrent on the lee side of the obstacle. If the Bernoulli lowering of pressure is sufficient to lift the obstacle up, the upcurrent in the eddy may maintain it in suspension for a time, since the eddy persists for a while even though the obstacle moves. The effect is only temporary, however, and the stone will soon sink to the bottom once more, but thereafter the process may be repeated. The stone thus progresses in the same direction as the current of water, in a series of jumps. Other effects also contribute. Round stones may simply be rolled in the direction of the current; flat stones may glide.

The faster the current flows the more marked will all these effects be, so that the lifting power of a stream will depend upon its velocity. The most violent currents are produced when waves break. Shingle tends, therefore, to be carried up beaches in heavy weather and deposited at higher levels, since the returning water flows less violently and is unable to carry the largest stones. Wave action thus tends to grade the shingle, leaving the larger stones high on the beach and the smaller stones and sand lower down.

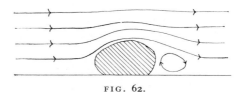

FIG. 62.

When waves strike a shore obliquely the shingle, which is continually being washed up and down, tends to drift along a beach. In some parts of the country, notably on the Dorset and Suffolk coasts, this process has given rise to long shingle spits. Off the Dorset coast is the Chesil Bank, a shingle bank some 9 miles long. In Suffolk the River Alde, originally joining the sea at Aldeburgh, has now been turned south and flows parallel to the sea for 10 miles before joining it at Shingle Street. Spits have also formed at the mouths of the Deben and Orwell but not to anything like the same extent.

Similar mechanisms are involved in the formation of river meanders. The strong currents on the outside of bends are able to transport materials which are deposited in the slacker water on the insides of other bends farther down. Much coastal erosion may be accounted for in this way, but the really destructive initial effect of high seas arises rather differently, though these other processes complete the work by transporting the loosened material away afterwards.

We return to the considerations of the last chapter. There is first an effect to be considered which is occasioned by the slowing up of the advance of the waves as they reach shallow water. This tends to crowd the waves together as they approach the shore, just as motor-cars get closer together where they are slowed down on hills. This concentrates the energy into a smaller volume so that the height of the waves increases. Since the destructive effect of the waves arises when they break and hurl masses of water at the coast, it will increase if the height of the wave increases although, of course, the average rate at which energy is carried to the shore by the waves is unaffected by their being slowed up.

It is in the process of breaking that the damage waves do is accomplished. Breakers are of two types, known as plunging breakers and spilling breakers respectively. The latter occur as the crests of the wave increase in height and become peaky. A piece of theory which is beyond

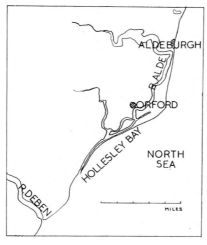

FIG. 63.

the scope of this book, shows that a crest becomes unstable when the peak contains an angle of less than 120°. The top then slides down the forward slope of the wave in a torrent of foam. Spilling breakers are formed on beaches which shelve gently and are the kind of breaker on which it is possible for surf riding to be practised. They are not, as a rule, highly destructive. The plunging breaker is caused by the crests of the waves overtaking the troughs. The leading slope becomes vertical and the top plunges forward into the trough in front. Pictures of both types of breaker are reproduced in Colour Plates VII–IX. Both types are very common and will be familiar to the reader.

Let us consider a wave advancing on the shore. Let us suppose its height to be 15 feet and for the purposes of a rough calculation, take its shape to be a simple wedge with plane sides as in Fig. 64. If its thickness is 50 feet its volume will be $15.50/2 = 375$ cubic feet per foot run along its front. This volume of water weighs 23,400 odd pounds or say about

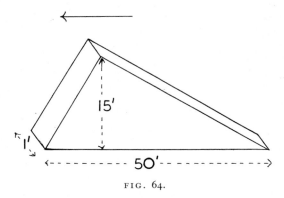

FIG. 64.

ten tons, and this mass of water will be hurled on to each foot of the shore with the wave velocity $c = \sqrt{gD}$

$$= \sqrt{15.32}$$

Its energy will therefore be

$$\frac{mc^2}{2} = \frac{23,400 . c^2}{2}$$

$$= \frac{23,400 . 15.32}{2} \text{ foot-poundals}$$

$$= 75 \text{ foot-tons approximately}$$

That is to say, the energy delivered by the wave is about 75 foot tons on every foot run of a sea wall built to receive it. It would lift one ton 75 feet into the air or 75 tons one foot. This energy has to be dissipated. If the sea-wall is sound the energy is used up partly in throwing spray high into the air and a good deal is returned directly to the sea in the form of a reflected wave. The energy of waves will be proportional to the square of their height so that if the height is doubled the energy delivered is multiplied by four.

The destruction which a large wave is able to bring about is not, as a rule, occasioned by direct battering of the sea wall, if that is the obstacle the wave finds in its path, though this has its effect, principally in loosening components of the wall or other obstacle. When a breaker plunges into the trough in front of it, air is trapped beneath it. With the tremendous momentum of the wave behind it, it becomes subjected to large compression and its pressure rises. The effect of this high pressure air may be seen by watching the spray cast up by a breaker. It is propelled by the compressed air beneath it and photographs seem to show that it starts with an upward acceleration as this air expands. The compressed air is able to find its way into any crevice in the structure meeting the waves, and blows out the material of which it is constructed. The momentum of succeeding waves is able to shift the pieces thus loosened from their anchorage and the work of destruction is completed.

It is particularly important that sea-walls and breakwaters, which have to withstand breakers, should possess smooth surfaces, free from cracks and crevices. If possible they should be built in water which is deep enough for the waves not to break at any state of the tide.

The energy possessed by sea waves is very large and if it proved possible to harness it, it might provide an answer to many problems connected with man's supply of energy. In spite of many attempts to do so, however, it has not been accomplished successfully so far. If we take the example of the rough sea, on which we made the approximate calculation above, we have 75 foot-tons delivered to each foot of the shore by each wave. If, in round numbers, we take these waves as arriving every ten seconds, the power supplied by the waves would be 7·5 foot-tons per second. Now a foot-ton per second is about four horse-power, so that we would have thirty horse-power per foot as the rate at which energy is supplied by the waves, or, since a horse-power is about threequarters of a kilowatt, 22·5 kilowatts per foot. A mile of coastline, therefore, would yield over 100,000 kilowatts, the output of a small electric power station. A very rough sea with waves of 20 feet would deliver about 180,000 kilowatts per mile. A sea in which the *average* height of the waves is 15 feet, however, is very rough—we were originally interested in the destructive power of big waves—so that 100,000 kilowatts per mile would probably be a generous estimate for the power delivered by an average rough sea. At sea, however, the energy crossing a mile at right angles to the direction of propagation of the waves, can reach double this figure. One of the problems to be faced in harnessing this energy is that the sea is not always rough so that the power supply from waves would be intermittent. A further serious difficulty is that it would be necessary to build any mechanism for utilizing wave energy sufficiently strong to withstand the worst storm conditions.

The advantage of placing breakwaters in deeper water, so that waves do not break against them, is that under these circumstances the waves are simply reflected. Their energy is returned to the sea in the reflected wave and it does not have to be absorbed by the breakwater. Intolerable

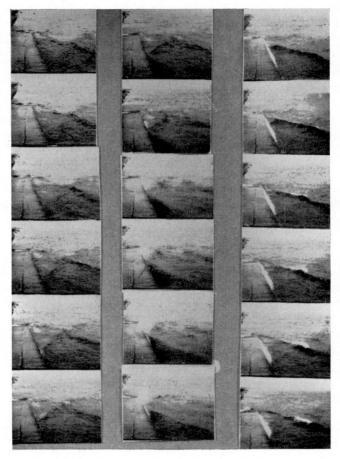

PLATE 16.—*Pictures from a ciné film showing the reflection of waves from a breakwater.*

stresses are not then imposed upon the structure. Plate 16 shows a series of pictures, taken from a length of ciné film, of waves being reflected from a sea-wall. The pictures also show how the incident and reflected waves are able to pass through each other without interference. Plate 17 is a still photograph of a similar reflected wave. When, as in this case, the wave is inclined to the sea wall, the reflected wave is also inclined at the same angle to the wall but in the opposite direction. This is further illustrated in Plate 18. When the waves are incident at right

PLATE 17.—*A reflected wave similar to that shown in the ciné film.*

angles to the wall they are reflected straight back. They travel back through the advancing waves so that offshore we have the interesting condition of water carrying trains of similar waves travelling in opposite directions. This is a well-known case of interference of waves

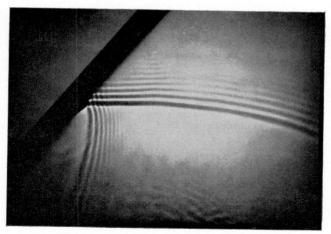

PLATE 18.—*Ripple tank photograph of the reflection of waves at a plane surface. The waves which are horizontal in the picture are travelling upwards. The reflected wave is seen leaving the obstacle and travelling to the right.*

and, on the sea, gives rise to the phenomenon known onomatopoetically as clapotis.

The addition of two trains of equal waves travelling in opposite directions produces standing waves which oscillate up and down without progressing in one direction or the other. The upper curves in Fig. 65 show five successive positions of a wave, A, moving towards the left. The middle picture similarly shows the positions of a wave, B, of the same amplitude and period, moving towards the right for the same

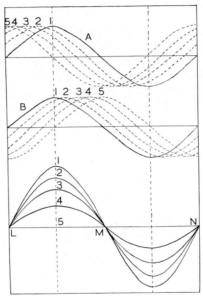

FIG. 65.

times. The bottom curves are obtained by adding together the displacements of A and B, taking account of their directions. In the position labelled 1, the two waves A and B coincide and their displacements add up. As A travels towards the left and B to the right, the resultant curve remains in the same position but decreases in amplitude. When A and B are in position 5, the crest of one falls on the trough of the other and complete cancellation results. The points L, M and N remain stationary and are known as nodes. As A and B continue to move the resultant curve swings below the axis between L and M and above between M and N.

The curves of Fig. 65 have been drawn using simple sine curves.

As a rule the waves on the sea do not possess this simple shape, and the motion of the water particles is not a simple up-and-down movement. The crests are also sharper and the troughs flatter than is the case with sine waves. The question of clapotis will be considered further in Chapter XIV. One result is that it is usually possible to see the two trains of waves travelling through each other and with a little practice standing on a breakwater, the reflected waves may be followed a considerable distance out to sea. As the crest of the reflected wave passes a crest of the oncoming wave, a displacement of very large amplitude is produced. The crests peak up to a height and an acuteness which

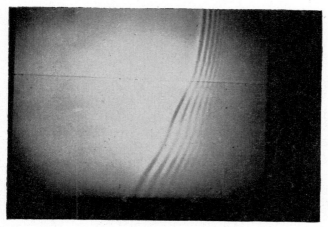

PLATE 19.—*Ripple tank photograph of the refraction of waves. A sheet of glass, tilted so that the water is shallow at the bottom of the picture, has been placed in the tank. The waves which travel to the right at the top of the picture are slowed down and bent back at the bottom.*

would be impossible in a travelling wave without its breaking. This produces the typical choppy nature of clapotis. It makes an unpleasant if not a dangerous sea in which to swim. The effects of reflection of the waves can be sensed in a ship a long way from the shore. In a voyage along a coast the movement of the ship is noticeably greater off a steep rocky shore, from which the waves are reflected, than it is off a shelving sandy shore where the energy of the waves is dissipated by breaking without much reflection.

Waves in shallow water are also refracted. Since they travel more slowly in shallow water than in deep, a wavefront approaching a shelving shore obliquely will have its inshore end slowed up, thus causing it to swing round and approach the shore more nearly parallel to it. Plate 19 shows this effect produced in a ripple tank. In a large shelving bay the waves will be found to approach the beach head-on, on all sides although their direction of travel on one side may be nearly opposite to that on the other. Because of refraction bays tend to provide shelter from the waves, whereas headlands tend to concentrate the wave energy on themselves. These effects can be understood by reference to Fig. 66. The energy from a wide front is directed on to a small perimeter of headland whereas that from a similar or smaller front may be spread round the longer coastline of the bay.

In equalities in the offshore sea-bed may also lead to similar concentrations of energy at certain points on a beach. It is often such concentrations which give rise to rip currents, the water, flung on to the land at these points of maximum energy in the waves, finding its way back

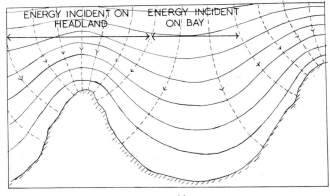

ENERGY INCIDENT ON HEADLAND   ENERGY INCIDENT ON BAY

FIG. 66.

opposite points where the concentration of wave energy is less. If the rip current flowing seaward from one of the sheltered sections of the beach is able to carve out a channel for itself in the sand, its effect will be to provide further protection to the sheltered section through the waves being refracted to the sides of the channel, as in Fig. 67. Energy is also concentrated upon neighbouring sections of the beach, thus again reinforcing the tendency for a rip current to form off the sheltered section. Once set up, therefore, such conditions tend to be stable.

The effect of shallowing of the water on the speed of surface waves is not important until the depth becomes a good deal less than the wavelength. It is sometimes said that the waves 'feel the bottom' when the depth is less than half a wavelength. At this depth the velocity of the waves has fallen by 0·4 per cent of its value in deep water. By the time the depth has decreased to a quarter of a wavelength, the velocity has dropped to 92 per cent of its value in deep water, and in water one-eighth of a wavelength deep it has dropped to 66 per cent.

What is meant by shallow water, therefore, depends upon the wavelength of the waves being considered. For waves with a wavelength of 100 feet the effect of the bottom does not become manifest until the depth becomes less than 50 feet. The waves forming the tides have wavelengths measured in thousands of miles and even the deepest ocean is shallow so far as they are concerned. Between these extremes come waves of very long wavelengths (several hundred miles) generated by seismic disturbances. Like the tides, their amplitude over the open ocean is small, amounting to only 1 or 2 feet. They are propagated with a very high wave velocity across the oceans corresponding to the depth of water, according to the expression $\sqrt{gD}$, and this may amount

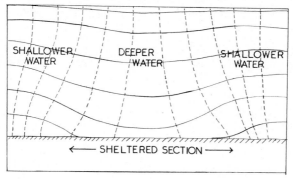

SHALLOWER WATER   DEEPER WATER   SHALLOWER WATER

← SHELTERED SECTION →

FIG. 67.

to 500 or 600 miles per hour. Their speed is sensitive to changes of depth occurring in quite deep water, and as a continental shelf is approached they are slowed down so that the energy they carry is concentrated into a smaller compass. Their height rises in consequence and it is thus that they take the form of disastrous 'tidal waves' which can devastate a coast. These tidal waves travel right across the oceans. The coasts of Japan, for example, were affected by waves generated by earthquakes near Chile.

The level of the sea is affected by winds and by changes in atmospheric pressure. It is well known that the sea will act as a kind of inverted barometer. An increase in the pressure of the atmosphere will depress the surface of the sea. A change in barometric pressure of $1\frac{1}{2}$ inches corresponds to a difference in water level of 20 inches. The sea, of course, will not respond instantaneously to pressure changes in the air above it because of its inertia. If an increase in atmospheric pressure could be suddenly applied or removed, a wave travelling with the velocity $\sqrt{gD}$ would spread out. If the area of increased atmospheric pressure happened also to travel with this velocity, the waves it starts at various points of its path would reinforce each other. The sea will, in a sense, resonate to the moving disturbance and large amplitudes in oscillation of the sea level could be generated. Over the open oceans, the velocity of propagation of long waves being 400 to 600 miles per hour, atmospheric disturbances cannot keep pace. The maximum rate of travel of depressions corresponds to a depth of about 50 fathoms. Normally depressions travel more slowly than this and are thus unable to keep up with the disturbance they produce in sea level, even in comparatively shallow seas. Fast ones can do so, however, in shallow seas and are capable of creating a wave of considerable amplitude. If the arrival of its crest coincides with high water it can lead to flooding. Hurricanes off the American coast moving with velocities corresponding to the propagation of waves in a depth of water found in this area, will create large oscillations, and much of the destruction associated with them is caused by the accompanying 'tidal wave', formed in this way.

Similarly, if changes in the wind occur in time with the natural period of oscillation of particular seas, the latter will be set into oscillation, and when the maximum of the oscillation passes points at the time of high water there, flooding can again occur.

Smaller bodies of water oscillate with shorter periods. Oscillations in harbours have been noticed, having a period of one or two minutes. It is thought that they may be caused by resonance to wave beats—the alternation between groups of waves with large amplitude and those with small.

Resonance to a moving atmospheric disturbance or to a change in wind occurring in time with the natural period of oscillation of a sea, gives rise to what are called surges. Flooding along the North Sea coasts of England and Holland has been caused by exceptionally high tides produced in this way. Many such floods have been recorded down to that which occurred on February 1st 1953. A particularly disastrous one took place in 1571. A violent tempest, with wind and rain, combining with an exceptionally high tide, did enormous damage. The damage from the storm was widespread and by no means confined to the East Coast. 'Maudlin' Bridge in Oxford was carried away and reports of damage came from Bedfordshire, Norfolk, Suffolk, Kent, Warwickshire and Staffordshire. It was particularly devastating in Lincolnshire. The sea walls, the construction of which had been initiated by the Romans, had been neglected from the time of the Nordic invasion. Holinshed gives the following account 'of the damage in the County of Lincoln,

PLATE XI.—*The formation of a wake by a light rowing boat.*

PLATE XII.—*The wake from a fast motor-boat in a river of limited depth.*

by the Tempest of Wind and Rain, which happened on the 5th October in the thirteenth year of the reign of Queen Elizabeth' (1571).

'Mumby Chapelle, the whole town was lost except three houses. A shippe was driven upon one house; the sailors thinking they had bin upon a rock, committed themselves to God; and three of the mariners lept out of the shippe, and chaunced to take hold of the house-toppe, and so saved themselves, and the wife of the same lying in child bed, did climb up into the toppe of the house, and was also saved by the mariners, her husband and child being both drowned. Likewise the church was wholly overthrown, except the steeple.

'Between Boston and Newcastell were three score sea vessels, as small shippes, craires, and such like, lost upon the coastes of Boston, Humerstone, Marshe, Chapelle, Tetney, Stepney, Newcots, Kelby and Grimsby, where no shippe can come in without a pilot, whych were all lost, with goodes, corne and cattell, with all the salt cotes where the chief and finest salt was made, were utterlie destroyed, to the utter undoing of manie a man, and great lamentation of old and young.

'Wentford [Wansford] Bridge being very strong, of eight arches in length, had three of the arches broken and clean carried away. Maister Smith, at the Swanne there, hadde his house [being three stories high] overflowed into the third storie; and the walles of the stable were broken down, and the horses tyed to the manger were all drowned. . . .

'Between Humerstone and Grimsby were lost eleven hundred sheepe of one master Spensers, whose shepherde, about mid-day coming to his wife, asked for his dinner, and shee, being more bold than mannerly, sayed he should have none of her; then she chaunced to look toward the marishes where the sheep were, and saw the water break in so fiercely, that the sheepe would be lost, if they were not brought from thence, sayed that he was not a good shepherde that would not venture his life for his sheepe, and so he went straight to drive them from thence; both he and his sheepe were drowned, and, after the water was gone, he was found dead, standing upright in a ditch.'

From Kent Holinshed reported: ' . . . at Erith breach, a mariner riding by the marishes, seeing two maidens in the marishes, and perceiving the waters breaking in so fast, that the maids were not like to escape, rode unto them, and one of them gat up behind him, and the other took hold of the horse's taile, and by that means were both saved from drowning. In the same marish were drowned a great number of sheepe. Also there in a marsh land that was sowne, were two boies keeping crowes in the afternoone, and seeing the water breaking in so vehementlie, gat them into a cart that was not farre from them, where they were faine to tarrie until the next tide, which came in so boisterouslie, that it had like to have overthrowne, both the cart and the boies.

H

And one of them being stronger than the other, kept the other in his armes, where he with cold, wet and feare, died: so that he was faine to let him fall from him into the water, when he perceived that he was past recoverie. A little from that place was also drowned a thousand sheepe and also manie other cattell.'

A great flood was also recorded in 1763 but in this case it seems to have been due entirely to continued heavy rains. In 1779 many vessels were said to have been driven nearly 2 miles into the 'Marsh' during the 'New Year's Gale', of that year. High tides have flooded the streets of Boston and entered the church, being 3 feet deep at one end on one occasion.

CHAPTER VIII

Bernoulli's Theorem

BERNOULLI'S theorem, which was mentioned in the last chapter, describes a phenomenon of such interest and importance that some further examples of it will be discussed in this chapter. It is also the basis on which any more advanced theory of waves has to be based. For most of the examples we shall consider, we need nothing more elaborate than the statement already explained, that *ceteris paribus*, the pressure in a moving fluid is least where it is moving fastest and vice versa. What is involved in the qualification *ceteris paribus* will be considered later in this chapter.

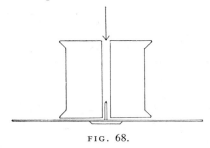

FIG. 68.

A very striking yet simple experiment depending upon Bernoulli's principle is illustrated in Fig. 68. A piece of card, about the size of a visiting card, is placed on one end of a cotton reel and air is blown by mouth down the centre hole of the reel, as indicated by the arrow. If the blowing is hard enough, the card, instead of being blown away, adheres to the end of the reel. The air is forced to move quickly in the narrow space between the reel and the card. Its pressure in this space becomes less than that of the air outside and the card is held up by the pressure difference. The card is apt to slide off if the face of the reel is not held exactly horizontally, but it can be prevented from doing so by pushing a drawing pin through it so that the point of the pin enters the hole in the cotton reel, as indicated in the figure.

A homely example of Bernoulli's theorem is provided by the Bunsen burner. Gas from the mains flows through a narrow jet at the bottom of the tube of the burner (Fig. 69). Its pressure is reduced because it is thus caused to move quickly and air from outside is entrained with it, the mixture burning at the top of the burner tube. Another example

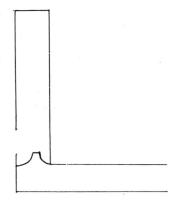

FIG. 69.

from the science laboratory is the water-jet aspirator with which a fair
vacuum can be obtained, if the velocity of the water passing through the
jet can be made high enough. The mercury or oil diffusion pump works
on the same principle and the arrangement for producing a blast in the
furnace of a steam locomotive is another example of the same thing.
Steam from the cylinders is blown up the chimney, thus sucking air
from the furnace with it and creating a draught.

A table tennis ball may be supported in a jet of air (Fig. 70). The
upcurrent in the jet is sufficient to support the ball's weight and the

FIG. 70.

fact that pressure is lower in the jet than outside, prevents it from falling out of the air stream. A photograph of a ball supported in a jet of air from a household vacuum cleaner is reproduced in Plate 20.

Another very interesting example is afforded by the drift of a spinning projectile. It is the effect of spin on the flight of a golf ball which causes the disconcerting drift to the right or left of the 'sliced' or 'pulled' drive.

PLATE 20.—*Ping-pong ball held stationary in an air jet.*

It is also the underspin on a well-hit drive which keeps it in the air and allows it to carry very much farther than it would have done without spin. There is a well-known story told of Professor Tait in this connection. By making measurements on golf balls and clubs he worked out the maximum distance it should be possible to hit a golf ball. Before publishing his results he, fortunately, discussed them with his son, who promptly described them as absurd, and went straightway into the field outside and hit a ball much farther. Professor Tait had neglected the effect of spin. It is a matter of common observation that in a good drive the ball is not projected at an angle of 45° to the horizontal as would

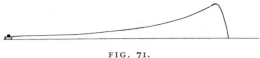

FIG. 71.

have to be the case to obtain maximum range in the absence of spin. A good drive has a low trajectory and floats in the air until its horizontal momentum is exhausted when it falls almost vertically to the ground, as is illustrated in Fig. 71. Its path indeed corresponds very closely to what was imagined to be the trajectory of all projectiles in the Middle Ages.

The explanation of this effect of spin is as follows. We reduce the flow of air round the golf ball to steady motion, in a very similar manner to that in which steady motion was obtained in the case of water waves. We give everything a velocity equal and opposite to that possessed by the ball so that the problem we have to consider is that of the flow of air past a rotating sphere. The situation is depicted in Fig. 72.

The rotating surface of the sphere tends to carry the air with it, with the result that near the upper surface the flow is speeded up, while near the lower surface it is slowed down. We thus have a region of high pressure beneath the ball and a region of low pressure above the ball. The ball thus floats in this pressure difference. When we remove the reverse velocity we see that the ball is supported on the crest of a pressure wave which it creates and which travels with it as it goes forward. The phenomenon is sometimes known as the Magnus effect. The markings on a modern golf ball are provided in order that it may get a 'grip' on the air as it rotates. It had long been noticed with the old smooth 'gutty' ball that its flight was much improved with age, as its surface became marked by cuts from the clubs. Players learnt to mark the surface of the ball to secure a longer carry and the modern marking was introduced to obviate the unfairness inherent in this haphazard practice.

The device of a rotating cylinder has been suggested, though never

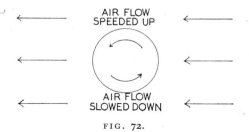

FIG. 72.

put into practice, as an aeroplane wing. It would have the advantage of freedom from stalling. Its lift would gradually diminish as the forward velocity decreased. The effect of spin in producing lift may easily be demonstrated with a small cardboard cylinder. A string is wound round it and attached to a stick, as in Fig. 73, so that when the stick is jerked forward the cylinder is projected with bottom spin. The effect can easily be sufficient to cause the cylinder to perform a loop, as indicated by the dotted line.

Between the wars a sailing ship, named the *Buchau*, was constructed to work on this principle. Two large vertical cylinders were mounted in place of sails. They were rotated by means of a small motor, about six horse-power being all that was required to do this. The driving

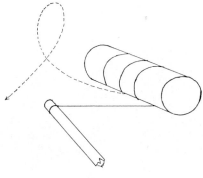

FIG. 73.

force was obtained from the wind. The vessel made trips across the North Sea, but the idea was not developed beyond this experimental model. A picture of the ship is reproduced in Plate 21.

Let us now discuss the theorem of Bernoulli a little more thoroughly, taking account of those other factors besides the velocity of the liquid, which may vary from point to point in the flow, and which we have so far neglected. We have, in particular, neglected the effect of gravity on the flow, and this is often the motive force which produces the motions. The necessary adjustment to allow for this is easy to make.

Bernoulli's theorem applies only to steady motion, that is to motion in which the streamlines remain fixed. Let the diagram of Fig. 74 represent a small tube of flow, the sides of which are formed by the streamlines. By stipulating that the tube should be small is meant that its area of cross-section is small. The tube may be of any length desired, so long as it is always bounded by the same streamlines of the flow. Suppose that the cross-section at the upper end A is α_1, the pressure

PLATE 21.—*The rotor ship 'Buchau'.*

there p_1 and the velocity of the liquid u_1. Let the heights of the two cross-sections at A and B be h_1 and h_2 respectively above some arbitrary level. Let us consider what happens as a very short length σ_1 of the liquid enters the stream tube at A and a corresponding short length σ_2 leaves at B. For simplicity we will restrict ourselves to the case when the liquid is incompressible so that the volume flowing into the tube at one end must be the same as the volume flowing out at the other. Bernoulli's theorem is simply a statement of the law of the conservation of energy as liquid passes in at one end and out at the other.

Let us draw up a balance sheet for the flow of energy into and out

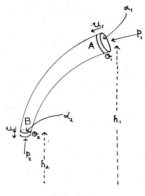

FIG. 74.

of this portion of stream tube. The volume of liquid which enters at A will be $\alpha_1\sigma_1$ and its mass will be $\alpha_1\sigma_1\rho$, if ρ is the density of the liquid. If it enters with velocity u_1 it will carry kinetic energy $\dfrac{\alpha_1\sigma_1\rho u_1{}^2}{2}$ into the section of tube.

The force exerted on the tube at A by the pressure of the liquid will be $p_1\alpha_1$ and in pushing the length σ_1 into the section, it will do work and thus introduce energy equal to

$$p_1\alpha_1\sigma_1$$

Now, we put in liquid at height h_1 and take out the same mass at a height h_2. This is equivalent to putting energy equal to

$$\alpha_1\sigma_1\rho(h_1 - h_2)g$$

into the section.

As the liquid emerges at B kinetic energy equal to

$$\frac{\alpha_2\sigma_2\rho u_2{}^2}{2}$$

will be carried away and work equal to

$$p_2\alpha_2\sigma_2$$

will be done against the pressure.   The balance sheet for energy input and output will balance if

$$\frac{\alpha_1\sigma_1\rho u_1{}^2}{2} - \frac{\alpha_2\sigma_2\rho u_2{}^2}{2} + p_1\alpha_1\sigma_1 - p_2\alpha_2\sigma_2 + \alpha_1\sigma_1\rho(h_1 - h_2)g = 0$$

If the liquid is incompressible $\alpha_1\sigma_1$, the volume of liquid entering must equal $\alpha_2\sigma_2$, the volume emerging from the section.

Dividing throughout by $\alpha_1\sigma_1$ or its equivalent $\alpha_2\sigma_2$ the relation reduces to

$$\frac{\rho u_1^{2}}{2} - \frac{\rho u_2^{2}}{2} + p_1 - p_2 + \rho g h_1 - \rho g h_2 = 0$$

or

$$\frac{u_1^{2}}{2g} + \frac{p_1}{\rho g} + h_1 = \frac{u_2^{2}}{2g} + \frac{p_2}{\rho g} + h_2 \quad . \qquad . \qquad . \qquad 22$$

This relation is known as Bernoulli's theorem.

If the velocity of the liquid u were generated by free fall through a height h, $u^2 = 2gh$, and the first term in Bernoulli's expression, $u^2/2g$, is the height through which the liquid would have to fall to generate its velocity. It is known as the 'velocity head'.

If the pressure p were to be generated by a static head h, $p = g\rho h$, so that the second term in the expression, $p/\rho g$, is the height of static liquid required to generate the pressure p. It is referred to as the 'pressure head'.

The height h, which measures the potential energy of the liquid, is called the 'potential head'.

Thus Bernoulli's theorem may be expressed in terms of these three different 'heads' (each expressed as so many inches, or feet or centimetres, etc., of the liquid). Put in this way Bernoulli's theorem may be stated as follows:

'Along any streamline in a liquid in steady flow, the sum of the pressure head, the potential head and the velocity head remains constant.'

The surface of a liquid in steady flow will always be a streamline. At the surface the pressure must also be atmospheric and will therefore remain constant. For the surface streamline, therefore, Bernoulli's theorem is reduced to the statement that

$$h + \frac{u^2}{2g}$$

remains constant along the surface in steady flow. If the height of the surface drops by an amount h, $\dfrac{u^2}{2g}$ must increase by the same amount. If the surface liquid started from rest, $u^2 = 2gh$. It, therefore, moves as though it were simply sliding over a smooth curve. This is the principle which we have used in our consideration of gravity waves on the surface of water.

An interesting example of the theory of shallow water waves is furnished by the flow of water over a weir, or waterfall, shown diagrammatically in Fig. 75.

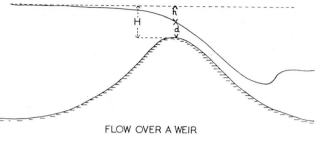

FLOW OVER A WEIR

FIG. 75.

Let us suppose that the depression of the liquid surface at the top of the weir, below that of the undisturbed water in the reservoir or river (assumed at rest) is h. Our previous reasoning shows that the velocity of the water coming over the weir will be given by

$$u^2 = 2gh$$

Now the depression in the surface may be looked upon as a wave on the water travelling towards the left relative to the water but held stationary by the adverse current of the stream. If d is the depth of water over the weir the velocity u of the water must therefore also be given by

$$u^2 = gd$$
or
$$gd = 2gh$$
i.e.
$$d = 2h$$

If the top of the weir is at a height H below the undisturbed level of the water we see that $d = 2H/3$ and $h = H/3$. The level of water at the crest of the weir is, therefore, depressed to a level below that of the undisturbed water by one-third of the amount by which the top of the weir is below the level of the undisturbed water.

If the rate at which water flows over the weir is Q cubic feet per second per foot run of the weir we shall have, assuming the other quantities are also expressed in feet and seconds,

$$Q = ud$$
therefore
$$Q = \sqrt{gd}.d$$
i.e.
$$Q = \sqrt{gd^3}$$
i.e.
$$Q = \sqrt{\frac{8gH^3}{27}} \qquad . \qquad . \qquad . \qquad . \qquad 23$$

which is a useful expression enabling us to determine the rate of flow of a river by simply measuring the height of the undisturbed water upstream of the weir above the level of the top of the weir.

At the base of the weir another wave is produced as the water slows up to enter the slower flowing water below. The water accelerates as it descends the weir and so will be travelling at a velocity greater than the velocity of waves in water of the depth coming over the weir. The wave at the bottom is, therefore, formed some little way away from the base of the weir where the depth is great enough for a wave to remain stationary against the flow of water. If this depth is not attained the flow is turbulent, as in a mill-race.

As an example of a case in which we cannot obtain the velocity of the water by the consideration of particles on the surface, let us examine the flow under floodgates, or sluices, which are opened at the bottom.

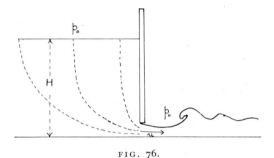

FIG. 76.

Let us consider the case of a large rectangular reservoir which is being emptied by opening a sluice, as in Fig. 76. The level of the surface of the water will sink, very, very slowly, so that it will be possible to neglect the square of its velocity. If we trace the streamlines of the water flowing through the sluice, back into the reservoir, they will be found to originate on the surface. The motion is not strictly steady but will be sufficiently nearly so to enable Bernoulli's theorem to apply.

The pressure on the surface of the reservoir will be atmospheric pressure p_0. The pressure in the jet below the sluice if small in height, will also be atmospheric or nearly so. Applying Bernoulli's theorem to a streamline at points in the jet stream and at the surface, we have

$$\frac{p_0}{\rho g} + H + 0 = \frac{p_0}{\rho g} + 0 + \frac{u^2}{2g}$$

therefore $$u^2 = 2gH$$

Thus the water issues from under the sluice gates with a velocity which is the same in magnitude as it would have been had it fallen through the height H. This fact is known as Torricelli's theorem.

Bernoulli's theorem is of wide application. It is, however, subject to one important condition. It is based, as we have seen, on the balance sheet of work and energy. The assumption is that energy is conserved as mechanical energy (either kinetic or potential) and not dissipated by friction. Frictional losses in liquids are caused by viscosity, so that Bernoulli's theorem can be applied only in cases where viscosity can be neglected. Fortunately the viscosity of many common liquids is small enough for this to be done as a first approximation in many cases, including many of fundamental importance.

Bernoulli's theorem applies to changes in pressure along streamlines only. There is a change in pressure also as we cross streamlines. This is determined by the shape of the streamline, the pressure gradient applying the forces required to cause the water particles to follow the lines of flow and to depart from their natural course of travel in a straight line.

CHAPTER IX

The Recording of Waves

THE systematic study of sea waves is something of very recent growth though observation of waves has, of course, been made for ages. Among the first to improve the quality of observation was Dr Vaughan Cornish. He accumulated a large amount of knowledge as a result of careful estimates of the height and period of waves, both from ships and the shore, and found a relationship between the speed of the waves and that of the wind generating them. It was not, however, until wartime needs directed attention to the possibility of forecasting conditions at sea and on the invasion beaches, that much progress was made. The science has thus grown up very largely since 1945, which year saw the publication of the first important paper by Barker and Ursell on the generation and propagation of ocean waves and swell. The British Admiralty formed a Swell Forecasting Section to study the conditions for the landings in Normandy.

Casual observation is sufficient to indicate that the height of waves varies over short periods. According to popular views every seventh, every tenth or every thirteenth wave is higher than the rest, but anyone who has attempted to check any of these statements will be aware that the pattern of the waves is more complicated and that the high waves do not come at precisely regular intervals. Waves, however, are very difficult to estimate by eye, and this applies even to their height unless some measuring pole is available, fixed to the bottom. It is particularly the case when observation is made from the deck of a rolling and pitching ship. Careful estimates of wave heights almost always appear disappointing, conveying little of the impression of immensity which the waves themselves produce. Newspaper reports of waves a hundred feet high are certainly exaggerated and most probably are occasioned by the dipping of the bows of the ship from which observation was made. Conrad once remarked that the size of waves depends upon whether you look down on them or up at them! The greatest height personally recorded by Dr Cornish was that of waves of 43 feet.

Progress did not become at all rapid until continuous records were made of waves and to do this some form of wave-recorder was required. The commonest method at shore stations is to place some device sensitive to the pressure of the water on the bed of the sea. Pressure variations, as the waves pass over the instrument, are then recorded, usually automatically by a pen moving over a travelling paper, as in a barograph. In using such a recorder it is necessary to remember that the pressure of the water at some point under a wave is not the same as that from a stationary head of water equal to the height of the surface of the wave above the instrument. What is recorded will depend upon the depth at which the instrument is placed relative to the wavelength of the waves. With very slow variations caused by waves of very long wavelength (the tides, for example), the static head will be registered almost exactly, but the variations are reduced to one-half when the depth is one-fifth of a wavelength. To measure 90 per cent of the 'static' fluctuations the instrument would have to be less than a twelfth of a wavelength from the surface, which for ordinary waves would be impracticable. The record produced by such an instrument, therefore, is not a true description of the surface of the sea. Short waves are lost entirely. Nevertheless, such instruments can be made very simple and

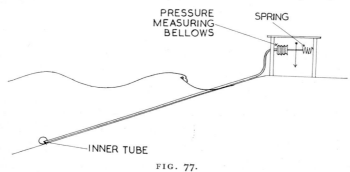

PRESSURE MEASURING BELLOWS

SPRING

INNER TUBE

FIG. 77.

can furnish useful data though care must be exercised in interpreting the results. The instruments have become, in fact, almost the standard apparatus for the study. Moreover, the loss of the shorter waves from the record is not always a disadvantage. Many of the points of interest arise from the study of the longest waves with which there is no difficulty.

The simplest device working on this principle can be constructed from a rubber bag, such as the inner tube of a small motor-car tyre, filled with air at a sufficient pressure to inflate it limply at the depth at which it is set. The rubber bag is sunk at the position where records are required and hose connects it to a pressure gauge recording on a rotating drum—see Fig. 77. It is important that the bag is not quite inflated at low water, so that the water pressures are able to deform the rubber, and it must not be completely flat at high water.

The pressure gauge can consist of pressure-measuring bellows working against a spring so that the pressure from the mean head of water is not registered. The device can be converted into a tide gauge by inserting a length of capillary tubing into the hose pipe. The rapid fluctuations in pressure caused by the waves are then not recorded but the instrument continues to register the slow variations caused by the tides. If a second pressure-measuring bellows is connected directly to the hose pipe and the two are arranged to oppose each other, as in Fig. 78, steady displacements caused by the tides will be backed off and only the waves will be registered.

The hose-pipe employed must be rigid and too long a length of it cannot be used because the air at the near end of the pipe would not then respond sufficiently to pressure changes at the far end. The National Institute of Oceanography uses canvas reinforced pressure tubing of quarter-inch internal diameter and finds that up to a hundred yards of it can be employed.

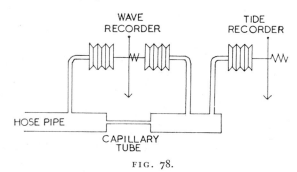

FIG. 78.

The 'Cambridge' pressure-recorder is a similar but more elaborate instrument. The pressure is measured electrically on the sea-bed so that longer lengths of connecting cable can be employed than with the simple hose-pipe instrument. The sea water operates a rubber pressure bellows, the movement of which is registered by an ingenious device known as a Shakespeare micrometer. Four coils of platinum wire are connected in a Wheatstone Bridge through which a sufficiently strong current is passed to heat them up. The arms AB and EF (Fig. 79) are fixed while CD is connected to the pressure-measuring bellows and moves up and down with variations in pressure. Upward movement of CD will cause coils AC and BD to close up and CE and DF to open out. The temperature of AC and BD rises, whereas that of CE and DF falls. The changes in the resistances of the coils brought about by these changes in temperature upset the balance of the Wheatstone Bridge and actuate a galvanometer on the shore, which can be made to give a record of the pressure changes. Slow variations caused by the tides

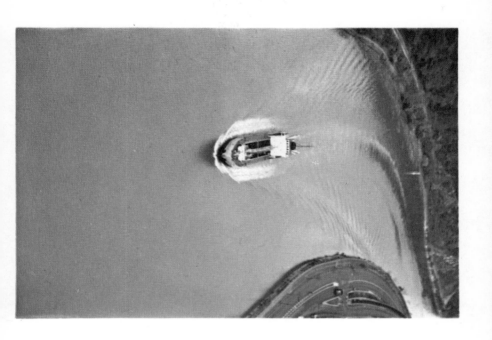

are eliminated by an electrically operated valve which admits air to the bellows equalizing the pressure inside with that of the sea water. It is closed when observations on the waves are to be recorded. Intermittent recording of waves in this way is all that is ever necessary. A continuous record would produce data so extensive as to defy analysis. The instrument requires a six-core cable to connect it to the shore.

The piezo-electric effect is also employed for recording sea water pressure. When crystals of quartz suitably cut are squeezed, an electrical potential difference develops over their faces. A wave recorder employing this principle comprises six crystals separated by steel plates. Pressure of the sea upon this pile of crystals develops an electrical potential difference, a head of between 20 and 30 feet of water being required to generate one volt. The two ends of the pile are connected to a condenser which is charged up. Changes in voltage are amplified by a valve enclosed in the instrument, further stages of amplification

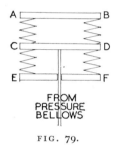

FIG. 79.

being added as required in the shore station. The instrument does not respond to slow fluctuations of pressure because a resistance is connected across the condenser which discharges it in times of the order of 10 seconds. This recorder requires a seven-core cable for connection to the recording station. The apparatus has proved reliable in use.

Attempts have been made to develop instruments which do not depend on pressure fluctuations but which will record the actual shape of the surface of the sea. None has proved satisfactory under all circumstances. Optical methods have been tried. A continuous ciné film of the surface registered against a calibrated pole erected on the bottom has been tried. A high recording position is required to prevent crests obscuring following troughs. Stereoscopic photographs have also been employed but all these methods require great labour to extract the data from the photographs and they all fail in bad weather. An inverted narrow-beam echo-sounder placed either on the bottom or supported beneath the surface has been employed. This records the actual height of the water surface above the instrument. It has two disadvantages

I

which become important in bad weather, which, of course, is the time when records are particularly desired. Spurious echoes arise from the sides of the waves when these are steep and when there is much aeration at the surface, as is often the case under storm conditions. Sometimes no echo may be obtained at all, the sound being lost by scattering.

Instruments designed to detect the position of the water surface electrically have been used. These usually require connections to be made to a pole fixed to the bottom. Thus the sea water may be used to short out the resistance of a wire below the surface so that a measurement of the resistance of the length remaining above gives the position of the surface. Similarly capacitors fixed at intervals to the pole can be shorted out as the water rises and change the frequency of an oscillator. Another method, which is on the whole more promising, is to measure

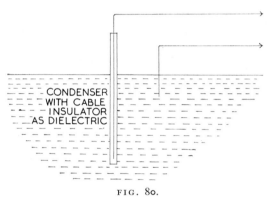

FIG. 80.

the capacity between an insulated cable, held in a vertical position attached to the pole, and the sea water surrounding it (Fig. 80). This method has been developed for recording small waves on lakes and in experimental tanks.

At sea, where there is no fixed platform from which to measure, the difficulties are greater. The difficulty in making reliable estimates of the heights of waves has already been mentioned. The best that can be done is to estimate the height relative to the waterline of the vessel and unless this is large enough it may be lifted bodily by the waves. Furthermore, the height of the waves is not the only information, or even the most important information, which is required. Sea waves are the resultant of the large number of wave trains of different amplitudes and wavelengths, travelling in various directions. They cannot often be successfully disentangled by eye and records kept continuously over a period are essential.

Use has been made of an airborne wave recorder which consists essentially of a radar altimeter with rapid response. Records are taken from an aircraft flying at about 200 feet above the sea. The aircraft speed is very high compared with that of the waves, so that what is practically an instantaneous record of the state of the surface of the sea along the line of flight is provided. Pressure recorders have been suspended below buoys floating in the surface by means of cables long enough to lower them into the undisturbed region below the waves. As the buoys rise and fall with the waves, the pressure recorders are carried up and down within the uniform water and they are thus able to record the height of the waves. Other types of pressure recorders may be held in a position below the waves, fixed by means of a drogue which is suspended beneath it in the undisturbed region of the water. These recorders then behave in a similar manner to a pressure recorder attached to the sea-bed. All these arrangements are based upon the use of the still water below the waves as a reference. The movement in deep water waves has fallen to half its value at the surface, at a depth of one-ninth of a wavelength, and to one-twenty-third at the depth of half a wavelength. The common run of waves in the Atlantic have wavelengths from 160 to 320 feet. In the South Pacific wavelengths up to 1,000 feet are encountered.

A great advance was made by the introduction of accelerometers into wave recorders. They are the essential component in the ship-borne wave recorder designed by Mr M. J. Tucker of the National Institute of Oceanography. The accelerometer enables the vertical acceleration of a ship or buoy to be determined, and from this an electrical device, known as an integrating circuit, can be arranged to register changes in the vertical position of the vessel to which the accelerometer is attached. These instruments, which are simple in principle, have been developed so as to be reliable and accurate in operation.

An accelerometer is simply a device for measuring displacements in the position of a mass suspended from a spring. Its method of operation can be seen from Fig. 81. E-shaped transformer stampings are wound with a magnetizing coil MM, so arranged as to magnetize the outer arms and the inner arm with opposite polarity. A magnetic field, which, apart from the stray field at the edge, is approximately uniform, is set up as shown in Fig. 82. In the uniform part of this field is suspended another coil CC (Fig. 81) which is attached to a heavy mass held on the end of a spring. It will be seen from Fig. 83 that as the coil moves up and down in the magnetic field a smaller or larger number of lines of magnetic induction will thread it. If the magnetic field is alternating, an electromotive force will be induced in the coil, which will be greater when the coil is lower in the field and more lines threaded, than when

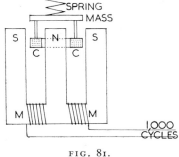

FIG. 81.

it is higher. This induced electromotive force, therefore, can be used
to indicate the position of the coil in the magnetic field. The coil is
attached to the accelerometer mass, mounted on the spring, so that if
the apparatus is given a vertical acceleration the weight will further
extend the spring when the acceleration is upwards and compress it
when it is downwards. The displacement of the coil will be proportional
to the acceleration and this is, therefore, also true of the induced
electromotive force, changes in which will be proportional to the displacement of the coil. Changes in the electromotive force induced in
the coil will therefore measure vertical accelerations of the instrument.
It remains to compute the actual vertical displacement of the instrument
knowing its acceleration. This is done electrically as has been already
mentioned.

The vertical velocity acquired by the instrument will depend upon
how long the vertical acceleration acts. If the acceleration is uniform,
the velocity is, in fact, the product of the acceleration and the time for
which it operates. Suppose the alternating electromotive force delivered
by the coil is rectified by means of a valve (i.e. changed from an alternating to a direct electromotive force E) and allowed to charge a large
condenser of capacity C through a high resistance R (Fig. 84). The

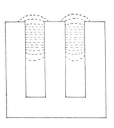

FIG. 82.

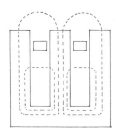

FIG. 83.

current flowing on to the condenser will be proportional to E if the condenser is allowed to charge up to a potential difference which is small compared with E. Thus the small potential difference e acquired by the condenser will be proportional to the product of E and the time for which it acts. Thus e will be proportional to the vertical velocity of the apparatus. Such a circuit which sums up the electromotive forces multiplied by the times for which they act, is known as an integrating circuit. Since the vertical displacement of the apparatus will be obtained by finding the product of the vertical velocity and the time for which it operates, a second integrating circuit to which the electromotive force e is fed, will give a measure of the vertical displacement of the apparatus. A combination of the vertical accelerometer and a double integrating circuit, therefore, can be made to keep track of the vertical displacement of a platform on which a pressure wave recorder is mounted. Adding pressure changes (or subtracting according to their direction) and vertical displacements will furnish a record of the wave motion of the sea.

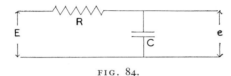

FIG. 84.

The vertical accelerometer used in this way was the basis of the ship-borne wave recorder designed by Mr Tucker. The instrument consists of two components, of which one is the accelerometer and the other is a pressure gauge. A hole is bored through the ship's side and the pressure gauge attached to it. Water pressure moves a diaphragm which in turn moves another coil lying in the field of an E-shaped electro-magnet similar to that in the accelerometer. The electrical outputs from the two components are added together so that the sum gives a measure of the height of the water surface above some arbitrary fixed level. Variations in the vertical position of the instrument, whether caused by rolling and pitching of the ship or its being lifted bodily by the waves, are thus taken account of by the accelerometer. Since the ship itself might shelter or reflect waves from one side, it is desirable to have two recorders, mounted one on each side of the ship, and wired in series. Then if waves are reflected by one side of the ship the wave-meter on that side will register double the amplitude while that on the other side will not register at all. The combined output of the two meters will, therefore, remain the same as if both were registering and reflection did not occur.

Such accelerometer wave-meters can be mounted in buoys, without it being necessary to refer the measurements to the undisturbed water beneath. An instrument so mounted will, of course, register the outline of the waves without the pressure component, since the buoy will ride on the surface of the sea.

It is not only desirable to have, for analysis, curves showing the displacement of the surface at a point. It is also desirable to know from what direction the waves are coming. These may be obtained by a ship-born wave recorder, by pointing the ship in different directions. At

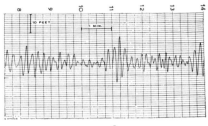

FIG. 85.

slow speeds the waves recorded do not appear to be much interfered with by the pattern of waves produced by the ship, and sufficient information can be obtained if the ship steers round a circuit such as a twelve-sided course.

The accelerometer is also valuable as a means of recording the motion of the ship itself and enables a study to be made of its behaviour under various conditions. It is hoped that such studies will prove valuable to the naval architect and lead to an improvement in ship design.

Fig. 85 shows a record taken with a ship-borne wave recorder. Wave recorders of this type have been used on the Royal Research Ship *Discovery II* since 1952 and in ocean weather ships since 1953. The diagram is reproduced by kind permission of the Royal Institution of Naval Architects, and may be found in Vol. 98 of their *Transactions*.

CHAPTER X

Wave Spectra

HAVING obtained records of waves by one or more of the pieces of apparatus described in Chapter IX, what is to be done with them? It is useful to know the maximum height of waves which can be expected at a given point, particularly from the point of view of the coastal engineer, but, on the whole, the raw records by themselves do not lead to a much greater understanding of the processes which are going on, without analysis.

The raw records show waves of various heights arriving on the shore, often in groups of high ones followed by a number of low ones. Popular views about the frequency of recurrence of waves of greatest height have already been commented upon. Small boats, such as lifeboats, take advantage of the quieter periods to get ashore in rough weather. As long ago as 1876, Stokes suggested that the phenomenon of wave groups might be caused by the interference of two trains of waves travelling in the same direction and with nearly but not quite the same wavelength. At certain points the crests of one train will fall on the crests of the other and the two combined will produce waves of large amplitude. Farther along the trains of the waves this will no longer happen, since the two trains do not fit exactly. After a number of wavelengths, depending upon the difference between the lengths of the two waves, we shall come to a place where the crest of one falls on the trough of the other, so that when they are combined together we get a resultant wave equal to only the difference between the component waves in height. The phenomenon is exactly the same as that of 'beats' in sound. It will be discussed in more detail in Chapter XVI.

In practice we might expect to find more than just two sets of waves coming in, and indeed bearing in mind the violent changes which occur in storm areas in which the waves originate, a whole spectrum of waves of different wavelengths would appear likely. It was not, however, until 1945 that the first analysis was made of a wave record and this was done by the Admiralty Swell Group already mentioned, in preparation for landings in the Far East where ocean swell is important.

The general picture of a wave record shows a mixture of wavelengths arriving. Fourier showed as long ago as 1807 that any curve can theoretically be broken down into a series of simple harmonic components (i.e. sine waves). At certain stations this analysis into simple constituents is, in fact, done by computation. The heights of the curve are measured at given intervals and special methods have been devised for obtaining the amplitude of the Fourier components. The process is similar to that used in the analysis of a tidal record except that, in the case of the waves, the theory provides no indication as to what periods are to be looked for. At the National Institute of Oceanography, a mechanical method was employed for many years to perform this task.

The bottom half of the wave record is blacked out by hand with an opaque paint (Fig. 86) and the record is made to traverse, at constant speed, a slit, behind which is a photoelectric cell. The other side of the record is illuminated so that a variable amount of light, proportional to the height of the waves, is stopped from entering the cell. The output from the photoelectric cell is amplified and applied to an oscillatory electric circuit, which resonates to a given frequency. The amplitude

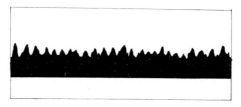

FIG. 86.

of the response of the oscillatory circuit indicates the amplitude of the component in the wave spectrum which is in tune with the natural frequency of the circuit. The wave trace is mounted on a drum which is rotated at a speed of 600 revolutions per minute and is then decelerated gradually to about 60 revolutions per minute, the deceleration occupying about 20 minutes. As the drum slows down each component contained in the wave record excites the oscillatory electric circuit in turn. The equipment which did much of the long work on waves is now largely replaced by digital computation.

Gravity waves in deep water differ from those in shallow water in being propagated with a velocity which depends upon their wavelength. The longer waves are propagated faster than the shorter. In the next chapter it will be shown that the velocity of propagation of waves in deep water is given by the equation

$$c = \sqrt{\frac{g\lambda}{2\pi}} \qquad . \qquad . \qquad . \qquad . \qquad 24$$

so that the velocity corresponding to any length of wave can be calculated.

When wave records made at a point on the coast are analysed, they frequently show components of long wavelength. These waves have long been seen to be present on occasion by direct observation, and are known as ground swell. Ground swell is composed of trains of long, low and regular waves. It has always been looked upon as a presage of the approach of storms. Waves of a variety of wavelengths are generated within a storm area. The longest travel quickest and so arrive at distant points ahead of the shorter waves generated at the same time. Under favourable circumstances the ground swell can be watched for considerable periods, during which the wavelength shortens as time proceeds and the shorter waves arrive. The ground swell and its shortening over a period of 2 or 3 days can be followed much more readily on a 'wave spectrum', that is an analysis into their constituent components of the waves arriving at the point of observation. The time taken for the ground swell to shorten in wavelength by a given amount, indicates the difference in times taken by the longer and shorter components to travel from their point of origin. Knowing, from Equation 24, the velocity of the two groups of waves involved, the difference in time of their arrival gives the distance of their point of origin from where they were observed. Barker and Ursell found, using this method, that the distance of the point of origin coincided, in many cases, with a known storm area at the time, to within 5 per cent. Spectra of the type from which they worked are shown in Fig. 87.

When the intervening areas have been free from storms, waves have been detected at shore stations from time to time, which have travelled enormous distances. The wave recording station at Perranporth has recorded waves which have travelled 6,000 miles from a storm area near the Falkland Islands. The first waves to arrive had a period of 21 seconds, which corresponds to a wavelength of about 2,100 feet. The velocity corresponding to this wavelength is, according to Equation 24, some 107 feet per second. This is the velocity at which the waves themselves travel, but there is a complication to be taken account of, which will be discussed in Chapter XVI, known as the group velocity of the waves. This is the velocity at which the energy of the waves is transmitted, and in the case of gravity waves on deep water it amounts to only half the wave velocity. The shortest waves to arrive from this storm had a period of 14 seconds, which corresponds to a wavelength of about 1,000 feet, and these waves would travel with a wave velocity of 72 feet per second. The group velocity of the longest waves was thus about 38 miles per hour, while that of the shortest was 25 miles per hour. The shortest waves arrived four days after the longest. Suppose

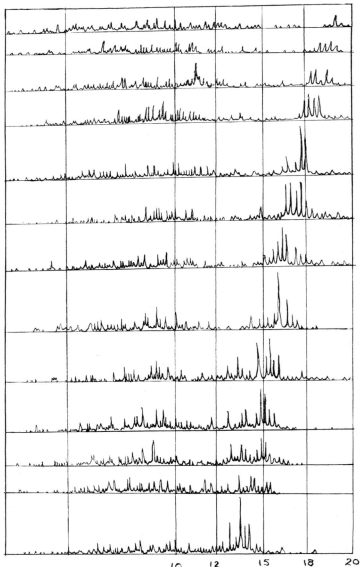

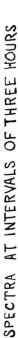

FIG. 87.

the longest waves had travelled for t hours and the shortest for $t + 96$ hours. Then, if they both came from the same point of origin, they must have travelled the same distance so that

$$38t = 25(t + 96)$$

giving

$$13t = 25 \cdot 96$$

i.e.

$$t = \frac{25 \cdot 96}{13} \text{ hours}$$

$$= 8 \text{ days approximately}$$

This is the time taken by the longer waves to travel from their point of origin. The shorter waves will have been travelling for approximately 12 days. The waves must therefore have travelled some 7,000 miles and have originated in the Southern Atlantic. The distance corresponds to that of the Falkland Islands.

Wave recording stations in California have similarly registered waves which had travelled all the way across the Pacific Ocean from New Zealand. This is a journey of similar length.

Except for the most recent American work, in which the direction of the waves was successfully measured, these records were obtained by simply recording the heights and times of arrival of waves at the station. Although it was possible to refer the waves to their point of origin, this was done solely on the estimation of distance. There was no indication of the direction in which the waves approached the station. For many purposes, as when it is desired to correlate the amplitude, velocity and direction of the waves with the direction and force of the wind generating them, it is desirable to obtain not only the overall spectrum of the waves arriving at a station but the spectrum of the waves arriving in each direction separately. This is by no means easy to do. It has been attempted from shore stations using three or four recorders, but the records so obtained are not very easy to correlate with each other. The method has been tried of obtaining a synoptic view of the surface of the sea at a given moment by taking stereoscopic pairs of photographs and then analysing them to give a plot of the sea's surface. The process of analysis is long and difficult and results are slow in coming. An accelerometer buoy with two gyroscopes to indicate tilt has also been used, and a radio altimeter used in an aircraft. Another method is provided by the ship-borne wave recorder. The ship steams on a series of selected courses and wave records are taken for each direction. The motion of the ship introduces a Doppler shift in frequency which varies with the direction in which the waves strike the ship. The direction of the ship for which this change in frequency is a maximum gives an indication of the direction from which the components of the wave system are travelling.

One effect of variation in the direction of travel of regular trains of waves is the production of the short-crested wave which is characteristic of storm waves. In place of the simple theoretical picture which we have used so far, of parallel lines of crests and troughs, what is found in practice is a series of waves the crests of which are limited in length. It is possible to consider a short-crested wave as the resultant of two long-crested components which are travelling in slightly different directions. At certain points the crests of one set of waves fall upon the crests of the other. The short-crested waves will be generated near these points. At other points the crests of one set fall upon the troughs of the other. These points fall between the short-crested waves. Short-crested waves are observed in or near storm areas. After travelling for long distances the two components separate, so that ground swell commonly consists of low long-crested waves.

The interest of many in the height of the waves upon the sea is derived from experiences of the motion of ships in a rough sea-way. It is only recently that attempts to correlate the motion of a ship with the amplitude, frequency and direction of the waves which give rise to it, have been at all successful. The problem is a very difficult one to attack, the object of those studying it being to provide the naval architect with sufficient information to enable him to calculate and forecast the behaviour of any ship under any conditions at sea likely to be encountered.

The most conspicuous motion of a ship at sea is rolling. This consists in the rotation of the ship about a horizontal axis running fore and aft. The next most obvious method of movement is that known as pitching. This is rotation about a horizontal axis running athwart ships, and leads to the rising and falling of the bows and stern. Combined with these conspicuous rotary motions are to be found linear movements as well. The ship may be lifted bodily by the waves, the movement known as heave. It may also be displaced bodily sideways or forwards or backwards by the waves. In addition the third possible rotation (about a vertical axis and known as yaw) may also occur. In the case of rolling, pitching and heaving, the motion is of necessity oscillatory. None of these motions could be continued indefinitely without disaster overtaking the vessel. If a ship be canted over in still water and released she will return to the vertical, and the same applies if her bow or stern is lifted and released. She will return to her normal attitude when the forces causing the displacement are removed. The same will equally apply if she was forced deeper into the water or lifted up bodily. In returning to the normal position after any of these displacements the ship would be expected to oscillate and she will thus possess more or less well-defined times of oscillation with regard to these motions. In view of the normal shape and dimensions of ships, common sense would appear to indicate that of these oscillations, that of rolling would last longest, while pitching would die out more quickly and heaving more quickly still. Thus the importance of the natural periods of oscillation possessed by the ship might be expected to be most important in connection with rolling, and least important in connection with heaving, with pitching intermediate between the two. There is some evidence that this is the case in practice.

The mechanics of the other movements is more difficult, but it is the rolling and pitching of a ship in a sea-way which constitute the main part of her movement. An investigation of the problems of the relation of the movement of the ship to the spectrum of the waves exciting it, was carried out both practically and theoretically by Cartwright and Rydill in experiments with the research ship *Discovery II*. With this vessel, which is slow, they found that the rate of meeting the waves was too low to excite her natural mode of oscillation in pitch. The vessel tended to respond most to waves which, in the direction in which the ship was travelling, had a wavelength about $1\frac{1}{4}$ times the length of the ship. In the case of rolling motion the effect of the ship's natural period was much more marked and she responded most to waves which were incident upon her sides with frequencies near to her own. This would be likely to prove true of the pitching motion also in the case of faster vessels which would meet the waves more rapidly.

Damage and delay to ships through waves makes it worthwhile exploring the possibility of routing ships so as to avoid the areas of bad conditions. By doing this the United States Military Sea Transport Service found it possible to reduce passage time by an average of 10 per cent. They employed predictions of conditions in the North Atlantic 3 or 4 days in advance, derived from the known distribution of storm areas, to plan optimum routes. This saving of 10 per cent of the time was the average for a thousand sailings.

CHAPTER XI

Waves in Deep Water

So far we have considered how waves in deep water may be recorded but have not developed any theory of how they might be propagated nor studied their properties. In this chapter we shall estimate their velocity and obtain a certain number of other useful relations, leaving a discussion of the results of observation until Chapter XII.

In the case of shallow water waves, which we have discussed so far, motion in the vertical direction was limited by the proximity of the sea-bed. The motion of the water particles was predominantly horizontal. In deep water this restriction no longer operates to modify the motion and vertical displacements are as important as the horizontal ones, even in the case of waves of small amplitude, to which we shall

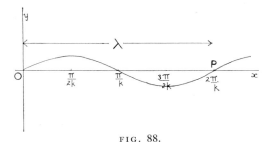

FIG. 88.

restrict ourselves. We shall assume in this chapter that the waves we are studying have a simple harmonic outline—this is to say, their surface can be represented by a sine or cosine curve.

We must first develop a perfectly general equation which is capable of representing such a wave propagated with any velocity c. Let us start by considering a stationary sine curve as plotted in Fig. 88. Its equation is

$$y = A \sin kx$$

When $x = 0$, $\sin x$ is also zero so that the curve passes through the origin. It increases as x increases until it reaches a maximum when $kx = 90°$ or $\dfrac{\pi}{2}$ radians and then decreases, becoming zero again when $kx = 180°$ or π radians. Thereafter it becomes negative and finally returns to zero at P, when $kx = 360°$ or 2π radians. The wavelength, λ, of the wave is the distance OP which is $\dfrac{2\pi}{k}$. We have, therefore, $k = \dfrac{2\pi}{\lambda}$ so that our original curve could have been written

$$y = A \sin \frac{2\pi}{\lambda} x$$

This curve is, of course, always in the same position. It does not travel forwards as a wave does on water.

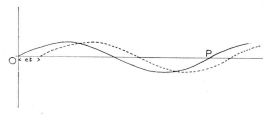

FIG. 89.

If the wave travels with a velocity c to the right it will have travelled a distance $c.t$ after a time of t seconds has elapsed. Its new position may be represented by the dotted curve in Fig. 89. Suppose the equation to this curve is

$$y = A \sin \theta$$

θ is here an expression containing x which we wish to find. We know that it will be zero when $x = c.t$ and that when $t = 0$ it must reduce to the same expression, $\dfrac{2\pi x}{\lambda}$, which we had before. The expression which does this is

$$\frac{2\pi}{\lambda}(x - ct)$$

Thus an equation which represents a wave travelling towards the right with velocity c is

$$y = A \sin \frac{2\pi}{\lambda}(x - ct) \qquad . \qquad . \qquad . \qquad 25$$

Any sine wave travelling towards the right may be represented by such a curve so long as c has the value of its velocity, λ that of its wavelength and A its amplitude.

When $t = 0$ the equation becomes

$$y = A \sin \frac{2\pi x}{\lambda}$$

which is the same as we had before. The wave, therefore, starts in the position of the solid line in Fig. 89.

We shall need to know the gradient of this curve at the points where it crosses the axis. Those familiar with the calculus can easily find this by differentiation. All we need to know to obtain it, is that when an angle is small the sine of the angle is the same as the angle measured in radians.

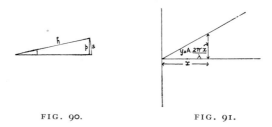

FIG. 90.   FIG. 91.

The angle measured in radians is the arc s (Fig. 90) divided by the radius h. The sine is the perpendicular p divided by h. When the angle is small these two values become the same.

Looking at Fig. 91 we see that when x is small

$$y = A \cdot \frac{2\pi x}{\lambda}$$

The gradient of the curve near the origin, therefore, is

$$\frac{y}{x} = \frac{2\pi A}{\lambda}$$

Thus if a particle travelled along the curve, near the origin, it would traverse a height $\frac{2\pi A x}{\lambda}$ vertically for every distance x it travelled horizontally. The ratio of its vertical to its horizontal velocity is, therefore, $\frac{2\pi A}{\lambda}$.

We can now return to the discussion of a gravity wave upon deep water. As before, we reduce the problem to one of steady motion by means of an adverse current which brings the waves to rest.

According to our previous consideration and Bernoulli's theorem, a particle of water will then travel over the waves as though it was sliding over a perfectly smooth switchback. It will acquire a high velocity in the troughs and will pass over the crests more slowly. Thus, as before, if it were not for the adverse current, particles would be travelling forward with the waves in the crests and backwards in the

PLATE XV.—*Reflection from the sun at low altitude.*

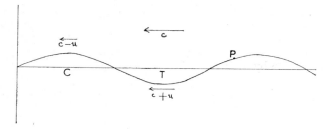

FIG. 92.

opposite direction in the troughs. On a crest or in a trough, furthermore, it would be moving horizontally. We shall assume that for a wave of small amplitude on deep water the motion is symmetrical and that if the particle moved forward with a horizontal velocity u on the crests, it will move backwards with the same horizontal velocity, u, in the troughs. Thus, when we add the velocity of our adverse current, travelling at a speed c equal and opposite to that of the waves, the particles in the surface must pass through the troughs with a velocity $c + u$, and over the crests with a velocity $c - u$ (see Fig. 92).

Applying the energy relation as before we would have

$$2mgA = \frac{1m}{2}\{(c + u)^2 - (c - u)^2\}$$

$$= 2mcu$$

giving $$g.A = c.u \qquad . \qquad . \qquad . \qquad . \qquad . \qquad . \qquad 26$$

On the crests and in the troughs the particles of water, as they stream over the waves, possess only a horizontal velocity. Now consider what happens as they cross the axis at the intermediate points such as P (Fig. 93).

Here their horizontal velocity will be intermediate between the

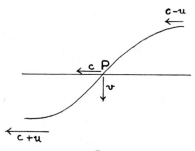

FIG. 93.

K

maximum $c + u$ in the troughs and the minimum $c - u$ on the crests, and if the motion is symmetrical, the horizontal velocity of the particle at P, as it crosses the axis, will be equal to c, the wave velocity. It will, however, also possess a vertical velocity, v, so that its resultant velocity V will be given by

$$V = \sqrt{c^2 + v^2}$$

The energy of the particle as it passes P will, therefore, be

$$\frac{mV^2}{2} = \frac{m(c^2 + v^2)}{2}$$

Again applying the principle of energy we have

$$mgA = \frac{m(c^2 + v^2)}{2} - \frac{m(c - u)^2}{2}$$

$$= \frac{m}{2}(v^2 - 2uc - u^2)$$

giving in this case $\qquad gA = \dfrac{v^2 - u^2}{2} + uc \qquad$.   .   .   27

but according to Equation 26 above, $uc = gA$, so that

$$v^2 = u^2 \qquad . \qquad . \qquad . \qquad . \qquad 28$$

Thus at the point P, surface particles, as they slide over the waves with the adverse current, will possess a horizontal velocity c and a vertical velocity u. But we found on page 130 that as it crosses the axis a particle travels $\dfrac{2\pi A}{\lambda}$ vertically for every unit distance it travels horizontally.

Thus $\qquad\qquad\qquad \dfrac{u}{c} = \dfrac{2\pi A}{\lambda}$

or $\qquad\qquad\qquad u = \dfrac{2\pi A c}{\lambda}$

But Equation 26 gives us

$$u = \frac{gA}{c}$$

so that $\qquad\qquad\qquad \dfrac{gA}{c} = \dfrac{2\pi A c}{\lambda}$

giving $\qquad\qquad\qquad c^2 = \dfrac{\lambda g}{2\pi}$

or $\qquad\qquad\qquad c = \sqrt{\dfrac{\lambda g}{2\pi}} \qquad$ 29

This equation for the velocity of the waves in deep water corresponds to the expression we deduced ($c = \sqrt{gD}$) for the velocity of waves in shallow water and has a similar importance. From it we can calculate a number of the properties possessed by deep water waves.

Unlike waves in shallow water, which all travel with the same velocity $\sqrt{gD}$ irrespective of their wavelength, the velocity of waves on deep water varies according to the wavelength of the wave. Long waves travel faster than short waves. A wave with a wavelength four times as great as another will travel twice as fast. From the formula we can determine the velocity of waves of a given wavelength and the calculation provides us with the figures in the following table.

TABLE III

Wavelength (λ) feet	Velocity of Wave	
	feet per second	miles per hour
5	5·05	3·4
10	7·14	4·9
20	10·1	6·8
40	14·3	9·7
80	20·2	13·8
160	28·6	19·4
320	40·4	27·6
640	57·1	38·9
1,280	80·7	55·0
2,560	114·2	77·9

When deep water waves enter shallow water their velocity is decreased and the waves tend to crowd together. That is to say their wavelength diminishes. Since, however, the number of waves passing through the shallow water does not go on continually increasing, it follows that as many waves must strike the shore in a given time as arrive at the shallow water from the ocean. The period of the waves, that is the time between the passage of successive crests, must therefore be the same in shallow water as it was in the deep, the lower velocity being exactly compensated by the shorter wavelength. In addition to a table giving the velocity corresponding to a given wavelength, it is, therefore, also useful to have one giving the velocity and wavelength corresponding to a given period. This is set out in Table IV.

This table follows from the fact that in one period the wave travels a distance equal to the wavelength λ. Thus if the period is T seconds and lengths are measured in feet,

$$c = \frac{\lambda}{T} \text{ feet per second}$$

TABLE IV

Period seconds	Wavelength feet	Velocity	
		feet per second	miles per hour
1	5·13	5·13	3·5
2	20·5	10·3	7·0
4	82·0	20·5	14·0
6	184·6	30·8	21·0
8	328·0	41·0	28·0
10	513·0	51·3	35·0
12	738·0	61·5	42·0
14	1,005·0	71·8	49·0
16	1,312·0	82·0	55·9
18	1,661·0	92·3	62·9
20	2,051·0	102·5	69·9

but
$$c = \sqrt{\frac{\lambda g}{2\pi}} \text{ feet per second}$$

giving
$$T = \frac{\lambda}{c} = \lambda \sqrt{\frac{2\pi}{\lambda g}}$$

$$= \sqrt{\frac{2\pi\lambda}{g}} \text{ seconds}$$

Thus
$$T = 0.436\sqrt{\lambda} \text{ seconds}$$

or alternatively
$$\lambda = 5.13\,T^2 \text{ feet} . \qquad . \qquad . \qquad . \qquad . \qquad 30$$

Further since
$$c^2 = \frac{\lambda g}{2\pi}$$

$$\lambda = \frac{2\pi c^2}{g} \text{ feet}$$

whence
$$T = \frac{\lambda}{c} = \frac{2\pi c}{g} \text{ seconds}$$

that is
$$T = 0.195c \text{ seconds}$$

or alternatively
$$c = 5.13\,T \text{ feet per second} \qquad . \qquad . \qquad . \qquad 31$$

It will be shown in Appendix V that the water particles on the surface possess a velocity which is constant in magnitude but which rotates steadily in direction. It is forward with the waves on the crest, backwards in the opposite direction in the troughs, and is vertically upwards or downwards as the wave passes through the level of the undisturbed water (Fig. 94).

To a first approximation the paths of the particles are circles. This, however, is strictly true only in the case we have been considering, of

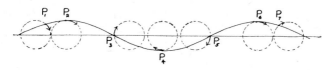

FIG. 94.

waves of which the amplitude is infinitesimally small. Actually, as the considerations of Appendix V indicate, the particles hold their forward velocity for longer than they do their backward. The paths of the particles are no longer closed, with the result that they advance slowly in the same direction as the waves, as in Fig. 95.

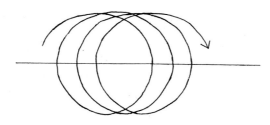

FIG. 95.

APPENDIX V

The Motion of the Water Particles in the Surface

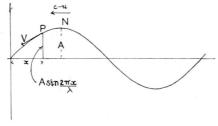

FIG. 96.

As before, let the waves, originally travelling to the right, be rendered stationary by an adverse current of velocity c to the left. We wish to investigate the velocity of a particle of water as it passes some point such as P, anywhere on the wave. When the wave is stationary its equation is

$$y = A \sin \frac{2\pi x}{\lambda}$$

Since the particle possesses a velocity of $c - u$ as it passes over the crest N, the velocity it possesses at P will be given by the energy relation which gives

$$V^2 - (c - u)^2 = 2gA\left(1 - \sin \frac{2\pi x}{\lambda}\right)$$

But

$$gA = uc$$

and therefore

$$V^2 - c^2 + 2uc - u^2 = 2uc\left(1 - \sin \frac{2\pi x}{\lambda}\right)$$

or

$$V^2 = c^2 + u^2 - 2uc \sin \frac{2\pi x}{\lambda}$$

If we wrote

$$\phi = \frac{2\pi x}{\lambda} - \frac{\pi}{2}$$

so that

$$\sin \frac{2\pi x}{\lambda} = \cos \alpha$$

we obtain

$$V^2 = c^2 + u^2 - 2uc \cos \phi$$

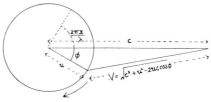

FIG. 97.

We can, therefore, easily make a geometrical construction for V as in Fig. 97. From it we see that the velocity of the particle, V, is composed of the velocity of the adverse current c and a velocity u, which is constant in magnitude wherever the point P may be. As the particle passes over the waves in the direction of the adverse current to the left, x, and consequently $2\pi x/\lambda$, decreases. The velocity u, therefore, rotates round the circle of Fig. 97 in a clockwise direction, remaining constant in magnitude all the time.

If now we remove the velocity c, of the adverse current, we are left with the velocity u as the velocity of the particle in the water surface.

The waves will travel to the right while the particle will travel to the right with a crest (when $2\pi x/\lambda = \pi/2$), backwards in the trough (when $2\pi x/\lambda = -\pi/2$), vertically upwards when passing through the undisturbed level (when $2\pi x/\lambda = 0$ or $-\pi$), and finally forwards again on the following crest (when $2\pi x/\lambda = -3\pi/2$). To a first approximation the paths of the particles are circles which they traverse with uniform speed.

This, however, will only be true if the waves are of infinitely small amplitude. In that case the velocity of the particle is small and when the adverse current acts, it travels with approximately uniform speed in the horizontal direction. Under these circumstances the angle $2\pi x/\lambda$

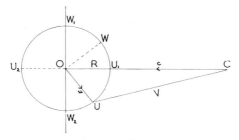

FIG. 98.

decreases uniformly with time and the velocity u will rotate with constant angular velocity, so that the particles will describe circles when the adverse current is removed.

Actually, however, particles flowing over the waves with the adverse current will not possess a uniform velocity along the x axis. The component of their velocity in the x direction will be given by CR (Fig. 98). It will be a minimum when U falls on U_1 (i.e. when W falls on W_1 and $2\pi x/\lambda = \pi/2$), and a maximum when U falls on U_2. The point U will thus pass over the left-hand half of the circle more quickly than it does over the right, and the particle velocity u, in the absence of the adverse current, will be longer directed to the right than to the left. The result will be that the paths of the particles are not closed and that they themselves gradually migrate to the right under the influence of the waves travelling in that direction.

CHAPTER XII

The Generation and Properties of Ocean Waves

WE have already, in Chapter IX, discussed the recording of the heights and directions of ocean waves and, in the course of doing so, touched on one or two of their properties. In this chapter we shall carry the discussion of their generation and properties further. First let us consider the height of the waves which can be expected.

Wave recorders have been carried by ships for only a comparatively short time so that really reliable records are very limited. A wave of 60 feet has been measured in this way and was thought to be sufficiently exceptional to deserve special mention when recorded. Dr Vaughan Cornish, in the course of very prolonged observation of waves, personally observed one of 43 feet as already mentioned. This was his maximum. He also quotes as exceptional the recording by the S.S. *Minnehaha* of a 41-foot wave in a strong gale, force 9, and he mentions an observation of 45-foot waves in a gale between force 9 and hurricane of force 12. Captain Wilson, in command of a Blue Funnel steamer of 12,000 tons, reported 70-foot waves in a storm of hurricane force (force 12). In all these cases the observations were made by experienced men with sufficient care to make their estimates reliable. The general run of waves met with, however, is fortunately much less high than these. For purposes of comparison the following tables are those used for official recording of observations. The first is the table of Beaufort wind speeds and the second is the Admiralty Weather Manual Table setting out a sea disturbance scale.

Waves generated in a storm area comprise a wide range of wavelengths, from ripples upwards, and they travel with different velocities, according to the theory of the last chapter. They also travel in a variety of directions. Combined together they produce a confused sea with no well-defined wavefronts travelling in a constant direction. Variations in direction of travel of the constituent elements lead to the formation of short-crested waves. The only practicable way of dealing with such a situation is by statistical means. When crests of a number of constituents coincide, a wave of large amplitude is generated. By treating the waves of a storm area as a random collection of constituent wave trains, it has been estimated that one wave in twenty-three is likely to be more than twice the average and one in 1,175 more than three times the average in height.[1]

[1] Deacon, *British Journal of Applied Physics*.

TABLE V. *Beaufort Scale of Wind Force, with Specifications and Equivalents*

Beaufort Number	General Description of the Wind	Specification of Beaufort Scale		Limits of Velocity in m.p.h. at about 30 ft above ground level
		For Coast Use*	For Inland Use	
0	Calm	Calm	Smoke rises vertically	Less than 1
1	Light air	Fishing-smack has just steerage way	Wind-direction shown by smoke drift but not by wind vanes	1–3
2	Slight breeze	Wind fills the sails of smacks, which then move at about 1–2 miles per hour	Wind felt on face; leaves rustle, ordinary vane moved by wind	4–7
3	Gentle breeze	Smacks begin to career and travel about 3–4 miles per hour	Leaves and small twigs in constant motion; wind extends light flag	8–12
4	Moderate breeze	Good working breeze; smacks carry all canvas with good list	Raises dust and loose paper; small branches are moved	13–18
5	Fresh breeze	Smacks shorten sail	Small trees in leaf begin to sway	19–24
6	Strong breeze	Smacks have double reef in mainsail	Large branches in motion; whistling in telegraph wires	25–31
7	Moderate gale	Smacks at sea lie to	Whole trees in motion	32–38
8	Fresh gale	All smacks make for harbour	Breaks twigs off trees; generally impedes progress	39–46
9	Strong gale	—	Slight structural damage occurs; chimney pots removed	47–54
10	Whole gale	—	Trees uprooted; considerable structural damage	55–63
11	Storm	—	Very rarely experienced; widespread damage	64–75
12	Hurricane	—	—	Above 75

* The fishing-smack in this column may be taken as representing a trawler of average type and trim.

TABLE VI
Sea Disturbance Scale
(*Admiralty Weather Manual*)

Code Number	Sea Disturbance Description	Mean Height of Waves feet
0	Calm; glassy	0
1	Calm; rippled	$\frac{1}{2}$
2	Smooth; wavelets	$1-2\frac{1}{2}$
3	Slight	5
4	Moderate	9
5	Rough	14
6	Very rough	19
7	High	25
8	Very high	31–37
9	Phenomenal*	45 or over

* As might be experienced in the centre of a hurricane.

Away from the storm areas the waves are propagated outwards like the waves from a brick cast into a pond. The brick sets up a confused pattern of oscillation in the water. The longer waves generated travel outwards faster, leaving the shorter ones behind, as has already been explained in connection with ground swell. The short-crested is replaced by the long-crested wave, since the interfering components which give rise to the former are propagated in different directions.

The Admiralty Navigation Manual gives the normal run of waves in the North Atlantic as having a period of six to eight seconds and a wavelength of 160 to 320 feet, with occasionally waves of 500 to 600 feet in wavelength. The former would travel with a velocity of 20 to 27 miles per hour and the latter at about 35 miles per hour. In the South Pacific waves of 1,000 feet are encountered, travelling at 50 miles per hour.

The longer waves of the South Pacific are accounted for by the fact that winds have a longer uninterrupted 'fetch' in which to generate waves. To develop the full storm waves of the North Atlantic a fetch of from 600 to 900 miles is required. A purely empirical rule connecting the height of the waves raised by storm winds with the speed of the wind, is known as Thomas Stevenson's law (after Thomas Stevenson, father of Robert Louis, 1864) according to which the height H of the waves, measured in feet, generated by storm winds blowing across a fetch of F miles, is given by the formula

$$H = 1 \cdot 5 \sqrt{F}$$

It has been found to apply over very wide ranges indeed by Dr Cornish, who tested it on the Round Pond in Kensington Gardens at one extreme, to fetches of hundreds of miles at the other. The formula does not mention the strength of the wind, except to say that it should be of storm strength, and obviously the formula can only be a rough guide. It indicates, however, the shelter to be expected from a lee shore. Off a lee shore the wind has not had sufficient fetch to generate high waves. Those which do arrive, do so against the wind from regions farther away. We shall see later in this chapter that a wind tends to damp down waves travelling in the opposite direction to that in which it is blowing, a fact which adds to the sheltering action of a lee shore.

The method by which waves are generated by the wind is not yet fully understood. Some of the first observations to be checked systematically, concerning the relation of the waves generated to the strength of the winds generating them, were made by Dr Cornish. He found that the velocity of the fastest waves produced in a storm approximated to the velocity of the wind. Thus he found the velocity of the waves generated in a storm of the intensity of a fresh gale in the Bay of Biscay, was 40 miles per hour, about the same as the speed of the wind. He also observed the periods of storm waves in Bournemouth Bay and was able to show that their speed in open water was a little less than that of the wind measured at land stations during the storm which gave rise to them. The longest period he observed in the waves in this position was 22·5 seconds, corresponding to the velocity in deep water of 78·75 miles per hour. These must be correlated with a severe storm occurring at a distance over the oceans. As a result of his observations, Cornish gave as an approximate relation, that the velocity of the waves is eight-tenths of that of the wind generating them.

He also observed the height of the waves generated by winds of different speeds and put forward another approximate relation that the wave height in feet is seven-tenths of the wind speed in miles per hour. The Scripps Institution, however, suggested as an empirical formula for the height of the waves in feet generated by a wind of U knots

$$H = 0 \cdot 026 U^2$$

The way in which the wind is able to generate waves on the surface of the sea, though not fully understood, can be discussed in an elementary manner. Very simple considerations would lead one to expect that, once started, waves would be increased in amplitude by a wind blowing over them in the direction in which they are travelling.

Fig. 99 shows a train of waves with a wind blowing over them in the same direction. In the region between A and B of the leading slope of a wave, the water will be rising while on the following slope, between B and C, it will be subsiding. On the simple assumption that the wind will exert pressures on these slopes as on a sail, it is obvious that the downward pressure will be greater on the following slopes, where the water is subsiding, as between *B* and *C*, than it will be on the forward slope, between *A* and *B*, where it is rising. The wind will, therefore, act in such a manner as to augment the movement of the water in the wave and so will transfer energy to it and the wave will grow. A wind will therefore cause waves to grow provided it travels faster than they do. A wind blowing against the direction in which waves are travelling will act in the opposite manner. It will press most strongly on the forward slope, where the water is rising, and less strongly on the rearward slope, where it is falling. The wind will therefore tend to damp down waves travelling in the opposite direction to that in which it is blowing.

Such a simple theory is capable of explaining a number of observations made beforehand empirically, upon the generation of waves. Thus

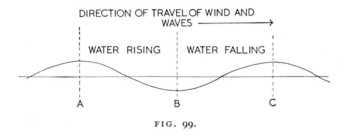

FIG. 99.

it would be expected that the longest wave which a wind could generate would be one travelling only slightly more slowly than the wind itself. This is in agreement with the speeds of waves observed to have been generated in storms of given intensities, such as those observed by Dr Cornish. Furthermore, the pressure which the wind can exert on the slope of a wave will depend on the relative velocity of the wind with respect to the wave. Since short waves travel more slowly than long waves, the wind will blow faster over them than over the long waves. It is to be expected, therefore, that the short waves could be generated more quickly than the long waves, as indeed is found to be the case. The short waves are generated quickly and reach their maximum, which is determined by the height to which they can grow before they break and dissipate their energy by generating turbulent motion in foaming crests. As the wind continues to blow, the longer waves grow in their turn. The energy in the wave spectrum is thus gradually shifted towards the longer wavelengths as time goes on. The longest waves will tend to predominate in the end, because they can store more energy.

The wind will also be capable of developing waves which travel at an angle to that in which it is blowing. It will then be the component of the velocity of the wind in the direction of propagation of the waves which will be effective in causing them to grow. It is to be expected, therefore, that the waves travelling in directions inclined to that of the wind will grow more slowly, and at any given moment will possess less energy in total than those travelling with the wind. The general picture, therefore, will be of a distribution of energy among waves travelling at angles with the wind but with the energy lumped in the forward direction. All this is in good overall agreement with observation. It is in the finer detail that much still remains to be done. It is, as yet, not possible to forecast what the state of the sea will be at a certain time later, given the meteorological data at a given time. To solve this problem it would be necessary to know, in detail, how air flows over the undulations of confused seas, what the turbulence of the air is like at a given moment and how it is affected as the waves themselves grow. It would also be

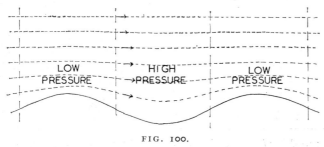

FIG. 100.

necessary to know more about the mutual interaction of waves of large amplitudes travelling in different directions and with different frequencies, and more about the effects of breaking.

The simple theory of wave generation which we have so far discussed has neglected the effect of the waves themselves on the flow of the air above them. The first effect of the undulations in the surface of the sea will be to cause the streamlines of the air-flow to be crowded together over the crests and to be spread out more widely over the troughs (Fig. 100). This will induce a Bernoulli effect similar to that which enables a water current to lift objects off the bed of a stream, as described in Chapter VII. The air will stream more quickly over the crests than it does over the troughs, and the effect would therefore seem to be to increase the elevation of the crests and the depression of the troughs and thus develop the wave system, though the situation needs a little more elaboration, as will be discussed later in this chapter.

When discussing tidal surges in Chapter VIII it was pointed out that a region of high atmospheric pressure depressed the surface of the sea beneath it and that if it were to be suddenly removed a wave would travel outwards. If then the pressure were to be applied at a point farther along, as the depression of the wave reached the point, the amplitude of the wave would increase. A region of high (or for that matter low) pressure, which travelled with the same velocity as the wave, would excite a kind of resonance and, in the absence of energy losses from other causes, would eventually generate a very large amplitude in the wave. The pressure differences set up over the waves by the Bernoulli effect are precisely of this kind and travel forward with the velocity of the waves. They thus keep pace with the waves and in this way would be able continually to add to their amplitude.

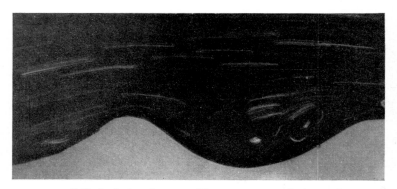

PLATE 22.—*Eddy in the lee of a wave. The water wave at the bottom is cut out in wood and the flow of air over it represented by a current of water carrying small pieces of metal foil. In a time exposure the foil indicates the streamlines of the flow.*

When the distribution is perfectly symmetrical, as in Fig. 100, and high pressure is applied all over a trough and low pressure all over a peak, the forces are, however, in fact, not being applied in a way which would augment the motion of the water. If the waves are travelling to the right in Fig. 100, the water is subsiding in the right-hand half of the trough and rising in the left-hand half. The high pressure is thus equally applied to subsiding and rising water. Similarly, over the crest, the low-pressure region would extend so as to include rising water on the right and subsiding water on the left. In spite of the promising beginning, therefore, a completely symmetrical distribution would, in fact, lead to the wind contributing nothing to the increase of the amplitude of the waves in this manner. It is as if, in swinging a child on a swing, we pushed him equally when he was coming towards us and when he was going away. To increase his swing we need to give our greatest effort as he goes away from us.

The first theory pointing to a possible way out of this difficulty was put forward by Jeffreys in 1925. It is known as his 'sheltering theory'. According to him, after the waves have reached a certain height the air-flow over them will no longer be symmetrical—an eddy will form in the lee of the wave. It is easy to show this happening in the case of a fixed model, as the photograph in Plate 22 shows. The waves on the sea are represented by the light-coloured part at the bottom of the photograph and are cut out of wood. The air which flows over them is represented by a stream of water flowing from right to left and it is seen that a marked eddy has formed behind the right-hand wave and a smaller one behind that on the left. (The streamlines of flow are rendered visible by taking a short time exposure of small pieces of chocolate wrapping

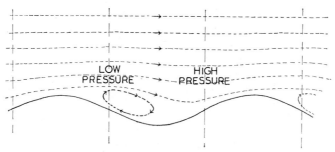

FIG. 101.

as they float past on the surface.) Such eddies would have the effect of shifting the high-pressure area farther up the following slope (the windward slope) of the waves, as shown in Fig. 101.

The region of high pressure will now coincide with that of the subsiding water. The low-pressure area will also be displaced to the right of the peaks and coincide more nearly with the region of rising water. The whole pressure system would be moved to the right relative to the waves where it would be able to impart energy to them.

However, it is doubtful how far this eddy formation is the correct explanation or, indeed, whether eddies form in the lee of waves at all. The model lacks one essential feature of the waves. When waves are rendered stationary by an adverse current the water then slides over them with the waves' velocity, so that the surface layers are in motion although the shape of the surface does not change. This movement of the surface water will communicate itself to the air immediately in contact with it. The velocity of the wind at the water surface will thus be reduced and could even be reversed.

The formation of an eddy will depend upon the existence of a strong wind blowing over the waves—i.e. on the relative velocity of the wind and the waves. The longest waves which a wind is capable of generating, however, travel with practically the same velocity as the wind and Jeffreys' mechanism can hardly apply in such cases. If there is a wind gradient the surface wind may be a good deal less than that which blows a short distance above the water.

Ocean waves are capable of travelling enormous distances once they have left the storm area where they originated. They thus must be capable of travelling through more or less still air without serious dissipation. One condition, therefore, which any theory must fulfil is that the process invoked to explain the formation of waves must not be reversed when the waves travel past still air—with the relative velocity between the air and the waves in the opposite direction. Otherwise the waves would be damped out in distances of a few hundred

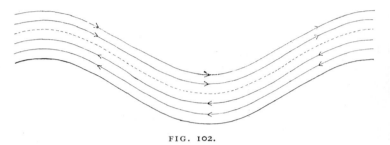

FIG. 102.

miles, equal in length to the fetch required to generate them. Two theories have recently been put forward which meet this condition.

Phillips has suggested that waves are generated by means of pressure disturbances travelling over the sea, those waves whose velocity is the same as that of the disturbance being built up by a process akin to resonance, as explained above. Large-scale variations in atmospheric pressure do not, as a rule, travel fast enough to generate very long waves. The approach of ground swell has long been a warning of the proximity of storms and it is evident that storm waves travel faster than the depressions which give rise to them. There is also, however, besides the large-scale pressure systems, a natural small-scale turbulence in the air blowing over a stationary surface. 'Waves' blowing over a field of corn are caused by eddies in the air crossing the field. Gustiness in the wind is also caused by them. Eddies are often generated by obstacles and are more prevalent overland than over the sea. Nonetheless, the smooth flow of air over an unruffled sea is something unknown in practice and a wind which reaches the sea from over the land is bound to possess

PLATE XVI.—*Reflections in a Scottish loch. The near sides of the ripples reflect the sky and produce lines of light across the water.*

considerable turbulence. Whether or not this can form a complete explanation of the formation of waves, the initial generation of waves of given wavelength may be due to these differences of pressure, consequent on atmospheric turbulence, which happened to be travelling with the wave velocity in a given direction.

The second theory is due to Miles who makes use of the velocity gradient of the wind, which blows harder aloft than close to the surface. If we take the case of waves which travel with roughly the same velocity as the wind, and bring them to rest by means of an adverse current, the air above them will also be brought more or less to rest as well. Because of the velocity gradient, the air just above the surface will actually be moving in the backwards direction. At a certain height above the waves there will be a layer of stationary air and above this the air will be moving forward. There will thus be a circulation and Miles traces the generation of waves to the pressures set up by the vorticity which is generated in the air and its convection by these currents.

How high a sea will grow depends upon the final dissipation of the energy once a steady state has been reached, as well as upon the forces available in the wind to generate the waves. Here exact knowledge is very limited. Breaking and the dissipation of energy in spray and foam is an obvious limiting factor. Waves break when they attain a certain sharpness in the peaks. It has also been shown that waves, initially irrotational, develop vorticity through viscous forces, and this will also dissipate wave energy.

L

CHAPTER XIII

Microseisms

THE earth's crust is in a continual state of vibration. The vibrations are sufficient to be a nuisance in the operation of sensitive apparatus. For example, when astronomical instruments have to be very accurately levelled one of the methods employed is to use a pool of mercury as a spirit level. The mercury is found to be always in a state of perpetual movement. The frequencies of the vibrations cover a wide range, from the high frequencies experienced as 'noise' by geophysical prospectors, to others with a period of a minute or more. The oscillations possess a vertical component and it has usually been assumed that they are due to transverse waves propagated through the crust, but it is possible that they could be mixtures of waves of different types.

Attempts have been made to distinguish recognizable groups of these disturbances on the basis of their periods. It is difficult to draw hard and fast lines. Attempts have also been made to classify them according to the cause by which they were originated. In most cases, however, the causes are obscure and cannot be identified with certainty, even if they are known at all. A group with periods of from about 3 to 8 seconds appears, however, to be fairly readily distinguishable at a wide range of stations.

Microseisms were first recorded by Father Timoteo Bertelli, of Florence, during observations extending over the years 1869–72. By 1874 daily observations were being made at five stations in Italy, and in 1884 at thirty. About the same time they were being observed in Japan and some ten years later in Germany. It seemed obvious that the whole surface of the earth was affected by these disturbances. There appeared to be a tendency for microseisms to be more marked in winter than in summer. There were periods, to which the name of microseismic storms was applied, when the amplitude of the oscillations was very large, separated by more quiet times. The oscillatory period, however, remained constant for several hours and the oscillations themselves continued for several days at a time. In 1905 Wiechert, in Germany, suggested that the cause of these microseisms was surf beating on a coast, which Gutenberg later suggested was that of south-west Norway. On the other hand, maximum amplitudes observed at Lemberg had been correlated by Laska rather earlier (1902) with the steepest barometric gradients in the atmosphere, that is with regions where the wind would attain its maximum velocity. Klotz in 1909 remarked upon the fact that 'a well-marked Low sweeping up the Atlantic coast from Florida to Newfoundland is almost always accompanied by marked microseisms. Microseisms are but slightly, if at all, influenced by the movements of Lows across the Continent.'

Early efforts to determine the direction in which microseismic waves were being propagated met with no success because it proved impossible to correlate the waves recorded at different stations. Shaw obtained some evidence in 1922, by using closely spaced recording stations, that microseismic waves at West Bromwich arrived from the north-west. In 1939 and 1940 Trommsdorf and Ramirez, using simultaneously timed tripartite stations, enabling accurate comparisons to be made of the times of arrival of individual waves, independently found that bearings so obtained indicated the position of a low-pressure area over the sea. The method was employed in attempts to track hurricanes off the North American coast, but it did not prove sufficiently accurate for operational use. In 1931 Imbo compared the frequency of the microseisms at Catania, in Sicily, with that of the sea waves in the Mediterranean. He found that the period of the microseisms was one-half that of the sea waves. This result was established again for microseisms recorded in England by Deacon in 1947 and by Darbyshire in 1950.

To complete the picture of these microseisms, obtained empirically, and to illustrate the facts which any theory of the phenomenon has to explain, a glance at some of the records may be helpful.

Fig. 103 shows a record taken at the National Institute of Oceanography. The upper record was taken when there were no storm waves in the North Atlantic. The lower trace was secured as a single depression approached our coasts.

A trace, less compressed along the time axis, recorded at the same place, is shown in Fig. 104. It shows the well-marked period which is characteristic of these oscillations. It will be observed that the amplitude is also subject to variations of the nature of beats.

Fig. 105 shows the results of an investigation by the Institute into the direction of propagation of the waves, correlated with the position of a storm in the North Atlantic. The direction of propagation has been corrected for refraction estimated to be caused by variation in the ocean depth.

This brief survey will serve to illustrate the principal facts connected with microseisms to be accounted for by a theory of their cause. Those theories which have been put forward so far have all been characterized by their connecting the origin of microseisms with some form of meteorological disturbance. There was first the theory ascribing them to the beating of surf on the coast, there were theories relating them to thermometric or barometric gradients travelling over continental areas

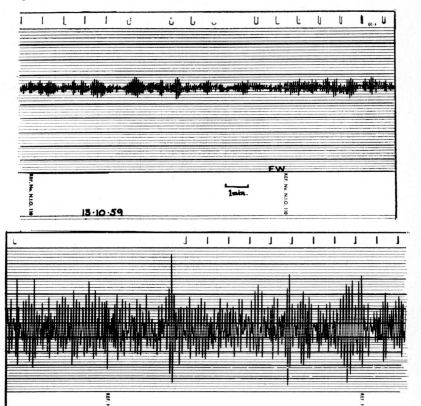

FIG. 103.

and there were theories connecting them to storms at sea. It does not follow that all microseisms are, in fact, generated in the same way, and indeed it seems likely that a variety of causes may operate in different cases. However, for the oscillations with periods of approximately 4 seconds, which have been shown fairly clearly to be associated with low-pressure areas over the sea off the coasts in both England and America, it seems clear that it is in that direction that it is necessary to look for an explanation.

The problem is to find a method whereby energy can be transmitted to the sea-bed from the atmosphere, via the water of the oceans. The

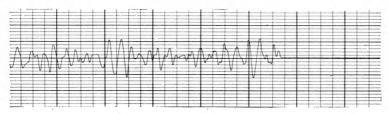

FIG. 104.

relation of the period of the microseisms to that of the waves would
appear to indicate that the latter are involved in some way, but the
periods of the microseisms approximate to one-half that of the waves,
so that it would not be likely that the action can be a direct one. Moreover, pressure fluctuations beneath waves are rapidly attenuated with

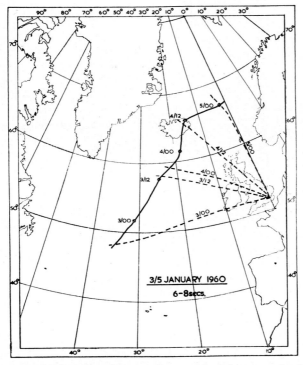

FIG. 105.—*The full line shows the approximate track of the centre of a depression
with the date and hour marked every 12 hours. The broken line shows estimated
microseism bearings, corrected for refraction.*

depth in the water and over the oceans become quite negligible on the sea-floor. Pressure variations are reduced to one-half their value near the surface when a depth equal to only one-fifth of the wavelength is reached and have diminished to only $4/1,000$ of this value at a depth equal to the wavelength. They have fallen to $1/14,000$ at two wave-lengths. In spite, therefore, of the enormous energy contained in storm waves it hardly appears likely that direct pressure differences beneath them can be the cause of microseisms. Waves with a period of 4 seconds possess a wavelength of only 82 feet, so that it is tolerably clear that

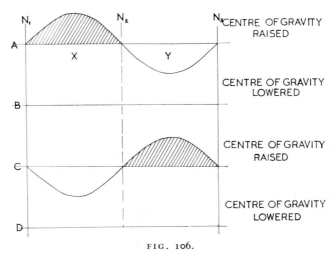

FIG. 106.

some other mechanism is to be looked for if the production of earth tremors capable of travelling a thousand or more miles within the earth's crust is to be accounted for.

These considerations led Longuet-Higgins to propose a new theory of the causation of microseisms by sea waves in 1950, which accounts satisfactorily for the facts and in particular for the period of the micro-seisms being one-half that of the waves. In place of travelling waves over the surface of the sea, for which the attenuation of pressure differences with depth is as given in the previous paragraph, Longuet-Higgins con-siders the case of standing waves, where the regime is quite different. The gist of Longuet-Higgins' theory is capable of being expressed very simply.

Consider the movement of the water when standing waves have been generated as in Fig. 106. A crest first appears at X, accompanied by a trough next door at Y. The crest at X subsides and the trough at Y fills up, leading to a surface which is level everywhere, as in position B. A trough then appears at X and a crest at Y, as in position C. After attaining a maximum these too diminish, giving rise once more to level water as at D. During the time when crests and troughs are present, the centre of gravity of the water is raised. In position A water from the trough at Y or its equivalent, below the undisturbed level, has been transferred to a position above the undisturbed level in the crest at X. In the position C the equivalent of water from the trough at X has been raised above the undisturbed level in the crest at Y. Thus the centre of gravity of the water as a whole rises and falls twice in every period of the waves. This movement of the centre of gravity of the water as a whole implies the presence of external forces acting on the water to produce the change in level. The only place from which such forces can be applied is through pressures at the floor of the sea.

If we have two simple trains of waves travelling in opposite directions, producing standing waves, then the pressure rises and falls simultaneously over the whole area. The sea will thus beat upon its bed with a frequency which is double that of the waves. The theory thus explains immediately why the periods of the microseisms are found to be half that of the waves of the ocean. It also explains how it is possible for wave motion, which varies from point to point, to give rise to oscillations of pressure which are in phase over wide areas and so able to generate waves in the sea-bed of amplitude sufficient to render their detection at large distances possible. In contrast, waves beating on a rocky shore would show no phase relationships. They might be expected to produce either oscillations of periods coinciding with that of the waves, or that of groups of waves, or alternatively, oscillations of very much shorter period derived from the impact of individual waves.

The further question remains, however, by what mechanism can stationary waves be generated by a cyclone? If it were possible for a cyclone to travel faster than and thus to outstrip the waves it produces, then those waves which it propagated ahead from an early position would meet those being propagated backwards from a later position. The fact which has been mentioned before, that ground swell is a harbinger of approaching storms, means that most storm areas do not, however, travel as fast, at least, as the longest waves they produce. Winds within a storm blow faster than the storm itself moves. On the other hand, however, some of the waves generated, at least, will not travel as fast as the storm. If microseisms of a period of about 4 seconds are in fact, produced by standing waves of a period of about 8 seconds, the wavelength of the latter will be about 300 feet and they will possess a wave velocity of about 30 miles per hour or rather less. However, the velocity which has to be reckoned with in this connection is not the wave velocity but the group velocity which will be only about 15 miles per hour. It is the group velocity which determines the rate at which the energy of the waves is propagated, as we saw in Chapter X, a point which is discussed more fully in Chapter XVI. Thus, to generate standing waves by overtaking waves it had already produced, a cyclone would have to travel faster than about 15 miles an hour. Cyclones move with all sorts of speeds but a velocity of about 30 miles per hour is not uncommon. That depicted in Fig. 105 appeared to be travelling at about 30 miles per hour. Very intense disturbances do not necessarily move faster than less intense ones. Hurricanes off the coast of North America travel not uncommonly at about the same speed. If the origin of the standing waves were of this kind, it would account for the fact that seismographic bearings obtained on cyclones appear mostly to follow the disturbances a little way behind. The microseisms, being generated by fluctuations of pressure on the sea-bed, would be expected to be propagated in all directions, irrespective of the direction of the waves generating them.

The standing wave theory of Longuet-Higgins accounts very convincingly for the regular 4-second period microseism. There are others, as has already been mentioned, the origin of which remains obscure. Microseisms of periods about 2 to 3 seconds have been investigated in the United States. In Texas they were found to arrive from the North, in New York State they arrive from the West and in North Carolina they come from the North-West. They must, therefore, have had a continental origin; they have since been shown, by Fr Lynch, to come from the Great Lakes. Oscillations of other frequencies await investigation.

CHAPTER XIV

Trochoidal Waves

IN the theory of waves in deep water given in Chapter XI, was included the assumption that the waves were symmetrical; that is to say, it was assumed that a trough was a mirror image of a crest and that the movement of the water in the crest was exactly counterbalanced by a corresponding motion in the opposite direction in the troughs. Midway between crest and trough was a position where the water particles possessed no horizontal velocity. In the end, however, it appeared that these conditions could only be met if the waves had infinitesimal amplitudes, to which the theory is, in consequence, limited.

Casual observation of waves running alongside a breakwater is sufficient to convince oneself that in practice troughs are not the mirror images of the crests and that the amplitude can be appreciable without there being any marked transport of surface water in the direction in which the waves are travelling. Casual observation also shows that the crests are sharper than the troughs, which are not only flatter but extend farther. The general appearance of the sea possesses some resemblance to the way waves used to be represented on some of the old portraits of sailing ships painted by the obscure marine artist for the sailors who sailed in them. In such asymmetrical waves the tendency for the water particles to spend longer on the crests, because they are then travelling with the waves, is offset by the fact that the crests are not as long as the troughs.

If a pencil is attached to a point on a wheel which rotates about a fixed centre, and a piece of paper is drawn past it at constant speed as it turns, it will trace on the paper a curve known as a trochoid. Alternatively, a trochoid may be defined as the curve traced out by a point on a wheel which rolls along the ground.

In Fig. 107 the wheel rolls towards the left and the path traced out by the point P attached to it, is shown by the full line P_0P, while the dotted line PP_1 is the continuation of the path which it will follow as the wheel rolls on. The curve thus traced out in that manner possesses narrow troughs and broad peaks, and to be useful as a representation of a wave on water, it would have to be inverted.

The shape of the curve varies according to the position of the point P on the spoke of the wheel. The two extreme cases are obtained when it falls either at the centre or on the circumference. In the first case, when P is at the centre, its path is a straight line, corresponding to an unruffled

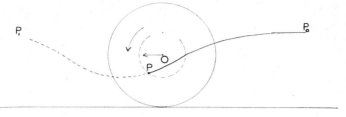

FIG. 107.

water surface. When P is close to the centre it traces out a curve which is very nearly the same as a sine curve and thus approximates to the case of waves of small amplitude, which has already been considered. The other extreme case occurs when P is on the circumference of the wheel. The curve which is obtained then is known as a cycloid. It is characterized by very sharp peaks culminating in points and, although in

FIG. 108.

appearance very reminiscent of the pointed waves in the old pictures, it is obviously an exaggerated form. Waves do not, in fact, attain that degree of peakiness. They break before they reach that stage.

Fig. 108 shows a collection of trochoids, drawn for a wheel rolling underneath the line O_1O_2 which will, of course, invert the curve of Fig. 107. The curves drawn in Fig. 108 are those traced out by various points on the spoke of the same wheel. The cycloid and straight line are the

FIG. 109.

limiting members of this family of curves. A trochoidal curve by itself, showing its main characteristics, is drawn in Fig 109. Its general resemblance to waves on water in cases where the amplitude is no longer small, is distinctly more promising than the simple sine curve.

Since, in trochoidal waves, the peaks are sharper than the troughs which are flatter and extend farther, the level of the undisturbed water does not lie half-way between the level of the top of a crest and the bottom of the trough. In the extreme case of the cycloid, the average water level is one-quarter as high above the troughs as are the crests.

The usefulness of the trochoid as a model for waves on water is not confined to the better shape which it produces for the profile of the wave. It was pointed out by Gerstner as long ago as 1802 that trochoidal waves can be propagated over the surface of deep water without change of form, without their amplitude having to be limited to infinitesimal dimensions. The particle velocity of the water needs no longer to be restricted to small fractions of the wave velocity, and we can consider cases more nearly parallel to what is observed in practice, where the two velocities, though different, are not of different orders of magnitude. Indeed, if the breaking of waves is to be considered, it is necessary to contemplate particle velocities which approach the wave velocity.

Although the cycloidal wave is not attained in nature it is, nevertheless, useful to consider the propagation of a wave of that form before passing to the slightly more complicated case of the trochoid. A wave of cycloidal shape is drawn in Fig. 110 by itself.

FIG. 110.

As in our previous theoretical discussions of waves, we will bring the wave to rest by means of an adverse current and thus reduce the question to one of steady motion. When this has been done once again the particles of water on the surface will be carried over the waves by the current, just as a particle would slide over a smooth switchback of the same shape. As they approach the crests, which are sharp, their velocity becomes more and more nearly vertical, and at the same time it diminishes as the particles climb up the wave. In the case of the cycloid, it is obvious that they must momentarily come to rest at each crest, since at the crests their velocity changes from being vertically upwards to being vertically downwards. The motion of the water particles over the waves will, therefore, be the same as that of a particle which started from rest at a peak on a smooth cycloidal switchback. We will now show that this is the same as the motion of the generating point on the circumference of the wheel (whose radius we will call k) so long as the wheel rotates with an angular velocity, ω, given by

$$\omega = \sqrt{\frac{g}{k}}$$

Let P be the point on the circumference of the wheel which rolls

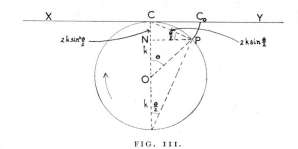

FIG. III.

underneath the line XY, generating the cycloid. If the point P started in contact with this line at C_0, when the wheel has turned through an angle θ it will have descended through a vertical distance equal to CN. From the figure we see that

$$CP = 2k \sin \frac{\theta}{2}$$

and

$$CN = CP \sin \frac{\theta}{2} = 2k \sin^2 \frac{\theta}{2}$$

Now C is the instantaneous centre. The point C of the wheel is in contact with the line XY and is momentarily stationary. The wheel is, therefore, for an instant turning about C. If the wheel turns with angular velocity ω, the velocity of P will therefore be

$$v = CP.\omega$$

$$= 2k \sin \frac{\theta}{2} \omega \qquad . \qquad . \qquad . \qquad . \qquad 32$$

But the particle has descended a vertical distance CN and its kinetic energy must be the work done on it by gravity in falling this distance, i.e.

$$\tfrac{1}{2}mv^2 = mg.CN$$

or

$$v^2 = 2g.CN$$

$$= 2g.2k \sin^2 \frac{\theta}{2}$$

But Equation 32 gives

$$v^2 = 4k^2 \sin^2 \frac{\theta}{2} \omega^2$$

whence

$$k^2\omega^2 = gk$$

and

$$\omega = \sqrt{\frac{g}{k}}$$

This is the result we wished to prove. So long as the wheel rotates with this angular velocity, the generating point P, on its circumference, will keep station with a smooth particle sliding over the cycloid under the influence of gravity, and this, in turn, corresponds to the motion of the surface particles of water when the waves are held stationary by means of an adverse current.

The wavelength λ of the wave is the distance rolled by the wheel in one complete revolution and is equal to the circumference of the wheel, i.e.

$$\lambda = 2\pi k$$

The time, T, taken to traverse this distance is the time taken for the wheel to make one complete turn at an angular velocity ω, i.e.

$$T = \frac{2\pi}{\omega}$$

The linear velocity of the wheel is therefore

$$c = \frac{\lambda}{T} = \frac{\lambda\omega}{2\pi} = \frac{\lambda}{2\pi}\sqrt{\frac{g}{k}} = \frac{\lambda}{2\pi}\sqrt{\frac{g}{\lambda}2\pi}$$

$$= \sqrt{\frac{\lambda g}{2\pi}}$$

This is the same value as we found for the velocity of sine waves of infinitesimal amplitude.

When we remove the adverse current, this velocity, c, becomes the velocity of the waves. The generating circle then rotates with its centre stationary. The water particle will still follow the generating point on the circle. Its path is thus accurately circular and there is no motion of translation as the particle moves with the waves.

We have now investigated the two extreme cases, namely those of sine waves of infinitesimal amplitude on the one hand and cycloidal waves on the other. For both we found that the velocity of propagation was given by the expression $\sqrt{\frac{g\lambda}{2\pi}}$ and for both the motion of the water particles was circular. We can pass from the one case to the other by allowing the generating point of the cycloid to take up various positions along the radius. When it is at the circumference it generates a cycloid and when it is near the centre it generates a sine curve of small amplitude. In intermediate positions the curves generated are trochoids. It is of interest to inquire whether the same properties apply to trochoidal waves.

In this case, however, we find ourselves confronted by a difficulty which we can only partially surmount by means of our elementary methods. When the generating point was situated on the circumference of the circle it became stationary when in contact with the line on which the circle rolls. Particles sliding over the waves also necessarily became stationary at the crests. This gave us one point at which the motions of the particles and generating point were the same, and if they coincided at this point our theory shows that they will coincide throughout.

With a trochoidal wave, on the other hand, particles pass the crests with a velocity which never becomes zero and there is no point where the two velocities must necessarily be identical. The best we can do is to show that the motion of the generating point corresponds to motion under gravity provided its angular velocity is $\sqrt{\dfrac{g}{k}}$. It thus represents a possible wave on the water surface, but we cannot show that other velocities are excluded. Let us first demonstrate that the generating point can be made to follow a particular particle moving under gravity and return to this point afterwards. We shall need to use the extension to Pythagoras' theorem in this, the proof of which can be found in any book on trigonometry. This theorem is that, in a triangle with sides of length a and b enclosing an angle θ the third side, c is given by

$$c^2 = a^2 + b^2 - 2ab \cos \theta$$

Let us call the radius of the wheel k, as before, and suppose that the point P, tracing out the trochoid we wish to consider, is at a distance A from the centre (see Fig. 112).

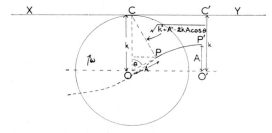

FIG. 112.

When P was at its highest point, P', it will be at a distance $k - A$ below the line XY and the wheel will have been turning instantaneously about the point C'. The velocity of P, when at its highest point, will, therefore, have been

$$C'P'.\omega = (k - A)\omega$$

Its velocity at any other point, as in the figure, will be

$$CP.\omega = \sqrt{k^2 + A^2 - 2kA \cos \theta}\; \omega$$

If the point P describes the trochoid as a particle of mass m sliding over the waves under the influence of gravity, then the increase in its kinetic energy as it arrives at P must be equal to the work done by gravity. Now P' is at a distance $(k - A)$ below the line XY. P is at a distance $(k - A \cos \theta)$ below the line XY.

Hence P is $A(1 - \cos \theta)$ below P'.

The work done by gravity on the particle in going from P' to P is thus

$$mgA(1 - \cos \theta) \qquad . \qquad . \qquad . \qquad . \quad 33$$

The difference in kinetic energies of the particle in the two positions is

$$\frac{m(CP.\omega)^2}{2} - \frac{m(C'P'.\omega)^2}{2}$$

$$= \frac{m}{2} \{(k^2 + A^2 - 2kA \cos \theta) - k^2 + 2kA - A^2\}\omega^2$$

$$= m(1 - \cos \theta)kA\omega^2 \qquad . \qquad . \qquad . \qquad . \qquad . \quad 34$$

The expressions, 33 and 34, will be equal, and therefore

$$m(1 - \cos \theta)kA\omega^2 = mgA(1 - \cos \theta)$$

i.e.
$$\omega^2 = \frac{g}{k} \qquad . \qquad . \qquad . \qquad . \quad 35$$

This is again the result we set out to prove. So long as the wheel rotates with the angular velocity $\sqrt{\dfrac{g}{k}}$ radians per second, then the generating point will pass over the curve of the wave as a particle travelling under the influence of gravity.

When we remove the adverse current so that the wheel then turns about a fixed centre, it follows that the generating point revolving round the wheel will follow a possible movement of the water particles in the wave motion, each of which would then describe a circle of radius A. We see from Equation 35 that the rate at which the generating circle turns is independent of the distance A of the generating point from the centre, and thus of the amplitude of the wave. It depends only on the radius of the wheel and this determines the wavelength of the wave. The wavelength will be the distance traversed by the wheel in one revolution when rolling under the line XY. It will be $2\pi k$. Thus we have

$$\lambda = 2\pi k$$

The speed of the wheel when following the adverse current is

$$c = k.\omega$$

and this is equal to the velocity of the waves (which is equal and opposite to that of the adverse current).

Thus
$$c = k \sqrt{\frac{g}{k}} = \sqrt{kg} = \sqrt{\frac{\lambda g}{2\pi}} \qquad . \qquad . \qquad . \qquad 36$$

Thus the formula for the velocity of these trochoidal waves over deep
water is the same as that of sine waves of infinitesimal amplitude and for
cycloidal waves.

It is possible for a particle to slide over a trochoidal switchback with a
range of velocities. Its velocity at the peaks must always be greater than
zero. If its velocity fell to zero at any point on the switchback the particle
would not possess enough energy to carry it over the crests. On the
other hand, it must not travel so fast that it jumps the crests. Between
these two values, however, lies a range of possible velocities. So far as our
simple considerations are concerned, any of the velocities in this range
could correspond to a possible wave motion. One of these velocities also
corresponds to our generating point on the circle turning with angular
velocity $\sqrt{\frac{g}{k}}$. When the adverse current is removed this particle moves
in a circle with constant speed.

The reader should be clear what has been and what has not been
accomplished by these various pieces of mathematics. There are two
motions to be determined, one the wave motion and the other the
motion of the particles. We need at least two conditions to determine
them. In the case of waves on shallow water, we were able to combine
the condition of continuity with that for the conservation of energy and
this combination gave both particle and wave velocities. In the case
of sine waves of infinitesimal amplitude we added the condition of
symmetry to that for the conservation of energy, and in that of cycloidal
waves there was the condition of vanishing velocity in the peaks under
the influence of the adverse current. It is difficult to find a second condition in the case of the trochoidal waves. We may, if we wish, assume
that the motion of the water particles is circular on the basis of experimental observation, or we may leave it as an interpolation between
the two cases of the cycloidal wave on the one hand and the sine wave
of infinitesimal amplitude on the other.

The latter view enables us to picture the process of the growth of
waves under the influence of the wind. The amplitude of the trochoidal
wave is determined by the radius A of the circle described by the generating point. The wavelength, on the other hand, is determined by the
radius of the circle, k, which rolls along the line to produce the trochoid.
As a wind puts more and more energy into a wave, the amplitude will
increase while the wavelength remains unaltered. The point P, gen-

PLATE XVII.—*Reflections in the river at Hereford. Vertical lines are prominent. Horizontal lines are lost. (Photo by Miss Judith Tricker.)*

erating the waveform, will thus move farther and farther from the centre of the generating circle. The form of the curve will, therefore, change from one which is approximately a sine curve of infinitesimal amplitude, when the amplitude is small, to the more peaky form as the limiting cycloid is approached.

Energy supplied by the wind goes to increase the amplitude in this way until it is dissipated by some other means. This happens when the waves break, for example. Let us calculate when our trochoidal waves will reach the point at which they break. As the waves grow, the particle velocity on the peaks will increase. When the particle velocity equals the wave velocity, the peaks will start to fall into the trough in front.

If the water particles attain the velocity of the waves on the peaks, then, when the adverse current is applied, they will be brought momentarily to rest in this position, since the adverse current has an equal and opposite velocity to the waves. This situation is just reached in the case of the cycloid. Simple considerations would thus lead to the view that waves would break when they become cycloidal. When that happens the amplitude will be given by

$$A = \frac{\lambda}{2\pi}$$

This means that waves would break when their amplitude was a little less than a sixth of their wavelength. In fact, waves break before they attain this point. More complete calculations show that the peaks of waves can never enclose an angle of less than $120°$, at which point they break. This calculation is based on the assumption that the motion is irrotational, which, of itself, excludes the cycloidal wave. Water has a low viscosity and whether rotational motion can be ruled out altogether is perhaps doubtful. In any case the practical value of this calculation is difficult to assess. Common observation, however, is sufficient to indicate that the extreme form of the cycloidal wave is not attained in practice.

The circular motion of the particles in trochoidal waves can be demonstrated by means of the composite photographs of the model in which the ball rolled along rails with a switchback wave formation, as in Plate 9. There are two ways in which this may be done.

The best method is to photograph the ball rolling over the trochoidal switchback with the ciné camera as before. The pictures are then projected on to a screen one at a time and photographed on to the same plate in a still camera. The ball rolling over the switchback simulates the motion water particles would have when the waves are made stationary by an adverse current. If, when the ciné pictures are projected for photographing in the still camera, they are moved laterally

M

by suitable equal amounts each time, the waves will progress between each pair of pictures and the effect of the adverse current can be removed. The picture on the plate in the still camera will then record successive positions of the particle in wave motion. The resulting picture, Plate 23, shows a series of positions which would be taken up by the ball were the wave to travel forwards. The path of the ball under these circumstances is seen to be approximately a circle. The ball which appears to lie off the circle in Plate 23 is caused by a ramp being used to project it along the wave with the necessary velocity. The first picture was recorded before the ball had quite left the ramp.

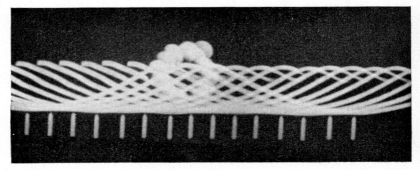

PLATE 23.—*Composite photograph to show the circular motion of water particles in wave motion. The picture was obtained from the same 8-mm ciné camera as Plate 10, but between each exposure the projected image was moved horizontally equal amounts to remove the effect of the 'adverse current'.*

If a ciné camera is not available a second method, which gives very good results, is to measure the positions of the ball in the original composite photograph of Plate 10, so that a white disc can be positioned accurately in the places occupied by the ball. This is done on a piece of black paper and successive positions of the disc are photographed on to another plate in the still camera. Between each exposure the paper is moved forward the correct amount so as to remove the adverse current, just as the projected images in the ciné projector were moved in the first method. A photograph obtained in this rather more cumbersome way is shown in Plate 24.

Before leaving the subject of trochoidal waves, we will return again to the question of clapotis, which has already been considered to some extent in Chapter VII. Then, to obtain the resultant displacement produced by two simple harmonic waves travelling in opposite directions, the expedient was adopted of simply adding the vertical displacements of the two waves at a point. This procedure, though giving approximate results, is inadequate even in the case of sine waves of small amplitude. In waves on deep water the horizontal and vertical motions of the particles are of equal importance and we ought not to concentrate on the latter and neglect the former, even though it is the vertical displacement which is most conspicuous. The displacements of a water particle caused by the two waves must be added vectorially, taking account of their directions as well as their magnitudes. However, even if we consider trochoidal waves, which can be propagated without change of form, we shall still have to limit ourselves to waves of small amplitude, since waves of large amplitude propagated across the same water do not

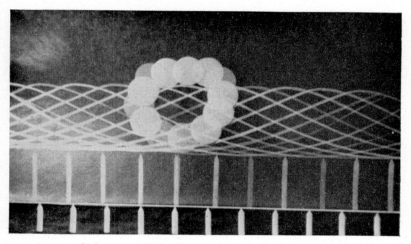

PLATE 24.—*A photograph of the disc in the same positions as in the previous plate but with the wave moved on between each exposure. The disc, which imitates the motion of the particles of water in the wave, moves in a closed path, approximately a circle.*

travel without mutually interfering with each other. The necessity for this restriction will be obvious as a result of the following consideration of standing waves or clapotis. Nevertheless, the limited investigation confined to waves of small amplitude is worth carrying out since it reveals important characteristics not apparent from the simpler treatment given earlier.

If we take the case of the interference of two equal trains of waves travelling in opposite directions, we find each water particle partaking in two circular motions, one rotating in the clockwise and the other in the counter-clockwise direction. The resultant of two such circular motions is a simple harmonic oscillation, as can be seen from Fig. 113, in which

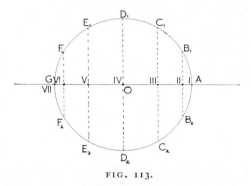

FIG. 113.

both movements start together at the point A and one rotates clockwise into the successive positions B_2, C_2, D_2 . . ., while the other passes through the positions B_1, C_1, D_1, . . . in the counter-clockwise direction. The resultant displacement will be represented by the points I, II, III . . ., except that it will be on twice the scale, since the two components in the direction OA will add together and the lines $O\,I$, $O\,II$, etc., will represent one of them only.

With waves on water, the interference of two equal trains travelling in opposite directions does not produce any nodes where there is a complete absence of movement. What happens can be understood from Fig. 114. This shows the transmission of two trains of waves travelling

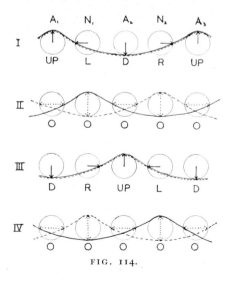

FIG. 114.

in opposite directions, one represented by a dotted and the other by a continuous line. The continuous line is drawn to represent a wave travelling towards the right and the dotted line one to the left. The wave travelling towards the right is generated by points rotating in the clockwise direction round the generating circles, and the dotted wave, travelling to the left, by points rotating in a counter-clockwise direction. In position *I* both waves coincide. The points under A_1, A_2 and A_3 possess a vertical displacement only, while those under N_1 and N_2 have a horizontal displacement only. Intermediate points will suffer both vertical and horizontal displacements but of smaller amounts. In position *II* the dotted wave has travelled a quarter of a wavelength to the left, while the continuous wave has travelled the same distance towards the right, corresponding to quarter rotations of the generating points. The displacements from the two waves are now equal and opposite under both the set of points A_1, A_2, and A_3, and N_1 and N_2, and the resultant is zero. This is true of all points along the water surface, which suffers no resultant displacement at this moment. After travelling a further quarter of a wavelength, the waves again coincide, as in position *III*. Position *IV* shows the situation after the waves have again travelled a further quarter of a wavelength. There are particles, therefore, which do not acquire a vertical motion at all, but oscillate in a horizontal plane, and particles which never possess any horizontal motion but oscillate in a vertical plane. Those which never acquire a vertical motion, nevertheless possess a horizontal motion; those which never acquire a horizontal motion possess a vertical one, and the horizontal and vertical motions which these particles acquire are both of the same amplitude. Particles situated between these positions oscillate in an inclined direction.

If we consider waves of finite amplitude instead of the infinitesimally small ones to which we have restricted ourselves so far, it becomes obvious that the two trains are no longer propagated as though the other was absent. For the assumption that they are would lead us to the conclusion that there would be times when the water surface would lie along the centres of the generating circles. As we have seen, the peaks of waves on water are sharper than the troughs, so that the level of the un-disturbed water must lie below the line of centres. At the time when the resultant displacement was zero, therefore, the water surface would lie everywhere above the level of the undisturbed water, which is ob-viously impossible. If we had a rectangular tank, shown in section in Fig. 115, in which there was a standing oscillation caused by the super-position of two trains of waves travelling in opposite directions, then the line of centres of the generating circles would lie along *AB*. There would, however, be only sufficient water in the tank to fill it to the undisturbed level *CD*. Clearly at no time can the water surface lie along the line *AB*. The two sets of waves do not pass through each other without mutual interference.

The fact that waves reflected from a breakwater can be traced out to sea through the oncoming waves, points in the same direction though it is inconclusive by itself. It might be possible to do this on account of the fact that two exactly equal trains of waves travelling in opposite directions are rarely to be expected. Waves arrive in groups and it might be that the reflected waves became distinguishable because they passed

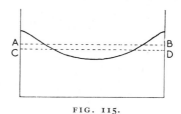

FIG. 115.

through incident waves of different amplitudes which would not produce annulment when crest passed through trough.

The fact that clapotis can peak up to an extent which would entail a travelling wave breaking, can now be understood. The travelling wave breaks when the particle velocity approaches the wave velocity. In a standing wave, there is no wave velocity and particles would not fall down into the trough in front as they would in the case of a travelling wave. At the antinodes in standing waves, the motion is entirely vertical. The shooting up of the crests into sharp peaks as the limits of the vertical motion is approached, is a familiar feature of clapotis.

CHAPTER XV

Eddies

THE resistance experienced by bodies moving through fluids is caused partly by the generation of eddies and partly by the generation of waves, in addition to frictional losses, which are due directly to viscosity. We shall leave the question of the generation of waves by bodies moving over the surface of water until Chapter XVII and devote this chapter to the resistance to motion entailed by the generation of eddies. We shall have liquids mainly in mind in the discussion, though much of what is said applies equally to gases.

In previous chapters we have made use of the concept of streamlines in studying fluid flow. These are the lines traced out by particles of the fluid as they are carried along by its steady motion. They may be rendered visible by smoke introduced into the flow in the case of gases, or by floating sawdust or other light small objects on the surface, in the case of liquids. With short time exposures the motion of these small particles can be rendered visible on a photograph. Small pieces of metal foil cut from a cigarette or chocolate packet serve admirably for this purpose.

It is important to notice that the shape of the streamlines will depend upon how they are observed. If the camera moves with the object they will not appear the same as when it follows the fluid. Plates 25 and 26 are two photographs of the streamlines of the flow of liquid past a plate. In the first the camera is held stationary relative to the plate; in the second it is held stationary relative to the liquid. The two appearances

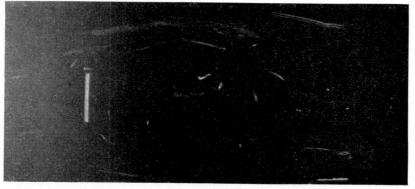

PLATE 25.—*Streamlines of flow past a stationary plate.*

169

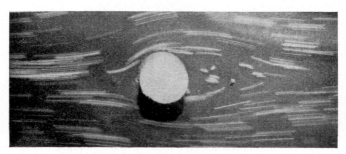

PLATE 28.—*The streamlines with the speed of the water a little greater. An incipient eddy is seen to form behind the cylinder.*

up plainly in the photograph in Plate 29 where the speed of flow has again been increased. With further increase in the velocity of flow, these eddies get carried away downstream one at a time alternating in the directions in which they rotate, those rotating in a clockwise direction being separated by eddies rotating in the opposite direction. When the camera is held stationary relative to the cylinder only those eddies which are attached to the cylinder are shown up by the closed curves of the particles. Those eddies which are carried away by the stream are evident only through the wavy nature of the traces left by the particles. Plates 29 and 30 are taken with the camera at rest relative to the cylinder, while in Plate 31 the camera is at rest relative to the undisturbed liquid. The eddies formed in the wake of a body moving through a fluid carry energy away from it and thus entail the body experiencing a resistance to its motion.

Eddies frequently form behind hills. When cycling against a head wind it is sometimes found, when ascending a steep hill, that the wind is reversed for a short distance and actually blows from behind, as in the diagram of Fig. 119. When this happens it usually occurs when the slope

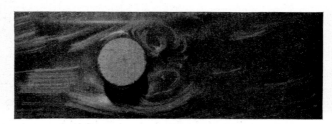

PLATE 29.—*The streamlines with a higher velocity of water. A pair of eddies has formed behind the cylinder.*

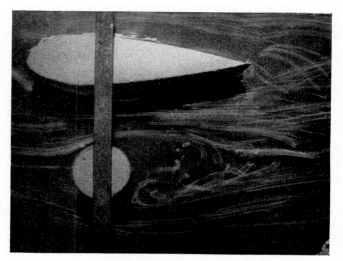

PLATE 30.—*The flow past a cylinder and a streamlined body which has the same width at right angles to the flow. One eddy has become detached from the cylinder.*

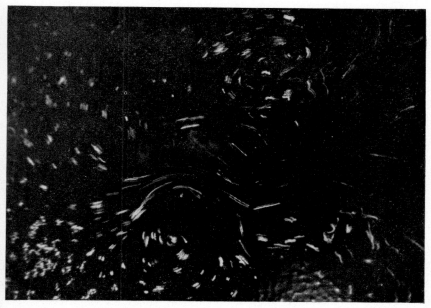

PLATE 31.—*The eddies formed in the stream behind the cylinder, photographed with the camera at rest relative to the water.*

173

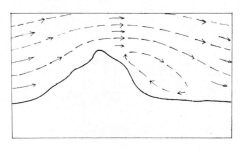

FIG. 119.

of the hill is too great, however, for the ordinary cyclist to reap much
benefit from it! He is usually to be found walking up the hill wheeling
his machine!

Osborne Reynolds investigated the flow of liquids through pipes. He
found that at slow speeds the flow was steady and obeyed the rules for
the flow of a viscous fluid known as Poiseuille's equation, the deduction
of which is to be found in books on physics but which we need not go
into here. As the speed of the liquid is increased, however, Poiseuille's
equation ceased to give a true account of what happened. This break-
down in the validity of a theory assuming straight line flow, occurred
suddenly, and Osborne Reynolds was able to show that it occurred
when eddies formed in the pipe. He was able to demonstrate this change
by means of a very beautiful experiment. He injected a stream of
coloured water into the centre of a pipe along which flowed a stream of
clear water. At slow speeds the coloured water was carried as a single
thread along the tube, but as the speed of the water in the pipe was increased there came a point when eddies suddenly formed in the tube.
The thread of coloured water was broken up and tinted the whole of the
rest of the water in the pipe. The transition is from a state of steady to
one of turbulent motion.

Osborne Reynolds' experiment is not difficult to repeat although it is
not easy to photograph. A small crystal of potassium of permanganate is
placed in a small inner tube which is held along the axis of a wider tube
by a wire mounting. The wide tube is connected to a supply of water,
care being taken to eliminate sudden changes in diameter which are
liable to generate eddies. Plates 32 and 33 are photographs of such an
apparatus in operation. In Plate 32 the stream of coloured water given
off by the small inner tube travelled steadily down the larger tube and
can be seen in the photograph as a dark streak. The velocity of flow of
the water was very small. In Plate 33 the velocity has been increased and
the coloured water mixed with the rest and become practically invisible.

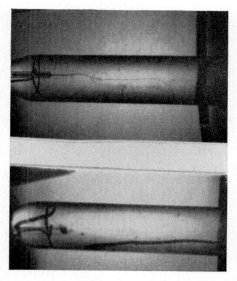

PLATES 32 *and* 33.—*Osborne Reynolds' experiment. A stream of coloured water is injected into the middle of a tube along which a current of water flows. When the flow is slow the coloured water forms a streak down the middle of the tube. When the flow is rapid eddies are formed which mix up the coloured water with the rest so that it becomes invisible.*

A similar change from steady to turbulent motion is often to be seen in the smoke rising from a cigarette, if the air is still. Plate 34 is a photograph of this happening. The hot air from the burning cigarette has a lower density than that of the surrounding air and is carried upwards by the resulting force of buoyancy. This causes the hot air containing the smoke to have an upward acceleration. While the ascent is slow the flow is steady, but as the air rises its speed increases and at a certain point the steady flow breaks down into turbulent motion.

It is the flow of air over the wing of an aeroplane which gives it its lift. When the wing is only slightly inclined to its direction of movement relative to the air, the flow over it is smooth for most of the width of the wing, eddies forming only at the trailing edge. The streamlines are compressed over the upper surface where the air moves fastest. The pressure here is thus lower than under the lower surface where the opposite happens. The wing thus possesses lift. The faster flow above the wing and the slower flow beneath it constitute a circulation of air round the wing. This circulation is maintained through the eddies at the rear, carrying away rotation in the opposite direction. As the inclination of the

PLATE 34.—*Eddies in smoke rising from a cigarette. The hot air and smoke rise from the cigarette slowly at first and the smoke forms a streak as in Osborne Reynolds' experiment. As the ascent is speeded up a point is reached where eddies form and the smoke mixes with the surrounding air.*

wing is increased, however, a point is reached where large eddies form over the upper surface. The smooth flow of the air is destroyed, the lift of the wing disappears and it is said to be stalled.

The production of eddies is influenced very markedly by the shape of the body causing them. It is not by any means always that the largest bodies produce the most or the most vigorous eddies for the same speed of travel through a fluid. Plate 30 shows the streamlines of liquid flowing past two bodies which each have the same cross-section at right angles to the direction of flow. The lower body is the cylinder used in the previous photograph. The upper has been 'streamlined' so that its section tapers only gradually. The cylinder generates much more vigorous eddies than does the streamlined body.

In this can be seen the advantage of the streamlined shape for bodies which have to move immersed in a fluid. The stirring up of the fluid in which they move, by reason of the eddies which they produce in their wake, is the main cause of the loss of energy which they experience, and this loss has to be made good, by engines or muscles, if the motion is to continue. Resistance to movement will be reduced, therefore, if the eddy motion in the wake can be diminished by streamlining the outer surface. It is an advantage in a vehicle that has to move rapidly through a fluid if bumps and excrescences can be avoided and eddies prevented from forming behind those parts which are unavoidably exposed, by rounding their leading surfaces and tapering those following by means of fairings. It is a most remarkable fact that birds and fishes, which are accustomed to move in this way through fluids, have evolved such excellent streamlined shapes. The evolutionary advantage of quite small changes of shape must have been sufficiently significant for natural selection to have fixed them in the inheritance of the species. Perhaps the most remarkable case of all is that of those mammals which have taken to water as their normal habitat. The whales, porpoises and seals have evolved very fishlike, streamlined profiles, and even such features for balance and propulsion as tails, flippers or fins. Many of them, like the whales, of course, have become so highly specialized that they are unable to survive if not surrounded and supported by their native element. The streamlined shape also appeals to us as an object of great beauty. Perhaps this has evolutionary significance too. On the other hand, it may be that it is the essential simplicity of line which gives the streamlined form its attraction. The shape of the birds is one that is particularly pleasing, and it is streamlining which introduces the element of beauty into so many modern forms of transport and other articles. Streamlining comes into our experience in many humble ways also. It is the basis, for example, of the superiority of the crawl over the breast stroke in swimming. When the legs are bent in the breast stroke, preparatory for the following kick, the thighs take up a position almost at right angles to the direction of travel. They act as a brake, effectively stopping the forward motion between the strokes. Though the forward drive per 'stroke' from the legs in the crawl is less effective than in the breast stroke, the very bad unstreamlined shape between strokes is avoided with considerable advantage to the forward progress. In air, streamlining becomes of importance only at high speeds, in spite of the fact that it is introduced in the design of objects which do not move at high velocities relative to the air in which they are immersed. Indeed, it is not uncommon for stationary objects to be streamlined because of the appeal of the simple lines thus obtained. Whether streamlining is of very great importance in the ordinary family motor-car is doubtful and

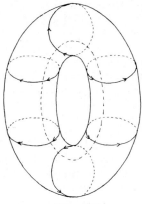

FIG. 120.

it has still probably to be defended on grounds of beauty of line rather than utility. The question of what constitutes beauty divorced from function is beyond the scope of this book.

An interesting case of an eddy is the vortex ring. This consists of a vortex filament more or less circular in form. The circulation in a vortex ring is shown by the streamlines in Fig. 120 which gives a perspective view of one. A vortex ring is formed when a puff of air is forced quickly through an orifice (Fig. 121) so that the outside of the moving air is retarded by contact with the edges of the opening. For the generation of visible vortex rings a box, such as a shoe box, may be fitted with a pliable side opposite an orifice cut in one side. To make the vortex visible the box is filled with smoke. When the diaphragm at the back is tapped, smoke-rings emerge from the orifice. The fact that the smoke remains in a ring as it travels forward indicates that the rotational motion is the property of certain particles of the fluid only. Vortex motion is not handed on from particle to particle like wave motion. Plate 35 is a photograph of smoke-rings made with a box arranged as in Fig. 121.

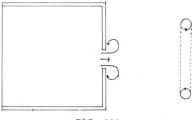

FIG. 121.

PLATES XVIII and XIX.—*Reflections in the Grand Canal, Venice. The green colour of the water of the canal shows in the reflections of the dark parts of the buildings. It is masked in the light reflections. (Photos by Mrs E. A. Holland.)*

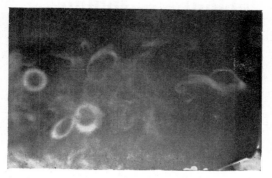

PLATE 35.—*Smoke-rings. These are ring-shaped eddies with the flow forward in the centre and backwards on the outside.*

Vortices are commonly generated when two streams of fluid travelling with different velocities merge, as may happen at the rear of an object round which fluid flows. There is a line, or narrow region, separating the streams (Fig. 122). The pressure on both sides of the line of discontinuity must be the same. The streams may nevertheless travel at different speeds, since they may have had different histories and have been subjected to different pressures. Relative to an observer on the line of discontinuity, moving with a velocity intermediate between those of the two streams, one stream will appear to travel to the right and the other to the left (Fig. 123). Such a condition is unstable. Suppose a slight protuberance to form on one side or the other of the line of discontinuity, as in Fig. 124. This will cause a spreading out of the streamlines on the concave side of the protuberance and their squeezing together on the convex side. This entails a higher pressure on the concave

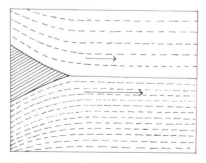

FIG. 122.

N

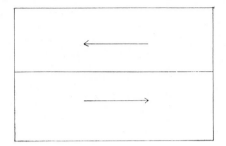

FIG. 123.

side and a lower pressure on the convex. The protuberance tends, therefore, to grow, and as it projects into the opposite stream it tends to be

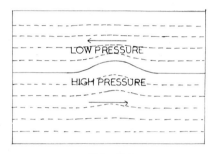

FIG. 124.

carried along by it. This imparts a rotary motion to the liquid and an
eddy is set up (Fig. 125).

This process is the basis of the formation of the eddies in the wake of
an aeroplane wing which gives rise to the lift, as discussed above. The

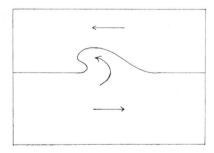

FIG. 125.

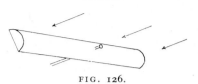

FIG. 126.

air, when it arrives at the wing, possesses no rotational motion and the wake is continually carrying rotational motion away in the form of eddies. This is only possible if some other part of the air is given an equal and opposite motion of rotation. The circulation round the wing which compensates for the rotational motion in the eddies, produces the lift of the wing in a manner very similar to the way a well-driven golf ball, which is given bottom spin which it communicates to the air close to it, receives its support. In the case of the aeroplane wing, the two streams of air which are concerned pass over the top and underneath it respectively. Their relative velocities depend upon the shape of the wing section as does, in consequence, the lift which the wing gives.

A toy which behaves very paradoxically depends for the explanation of its mode of action on the generation of eddies. It is possible to construct a windmill which will rotate in either direction in a stream of air. Its sails are perfectly symmetrical relative to the flow of the air. They consist of half a circular cylinder (Fig. 126) and can be constructed by dividing a piece of dowel rod lengthwise, so that the ends of each section are semi-circles. A pin is passed loosely through a hole in the centre of one piece and a bead threaded on to the pin to act as a bearing, so that the sails turn very freely. The pin is stuck horizontally into a piece of wood, to support the mill. When it is placed in a strong stream of air (for example, such as can be provided by a vacuum cleaner) and the sails set rotating with a smart tap, it will be found that they continue to rotate and indeed speed up rapidly, no matter in which direction the rotation was initiated. The explanation of this puzzling behaviour is as follows. When the half cylinder is introduced into the air-stream, a pair of eddies forms behind it, as in Fig. 127. When the sail is suddenly

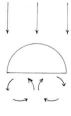

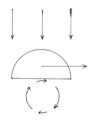

FIG. 127.   FIG. 128.

pushed to one side, one of these eddies becomes detached from the mill and drifts off in the wake, leaving the other behind the sail, as in Fig. 128. This gives rise to the Magnus effect, which continues to move the sail in the direction in which it has been set going. Once set going the sail gives rise to a stream of eddies like the aeroplane wing, which maintains the circulation and thus the motion. The whole affair being symmetrical, it will work equally well in either direction.

We must now return to a further consideration of the streamline flow of Fig. 118. It was remarked in connection with this figure, that if the fluid possessed no viscosity, the body would experience no resistance in moving through it, though its apparent mass would be increased. Streamlines of this form are readily obtained when the viscosity of the fluid is large. If the viscosity of the fluid is not negligible, the body would experience a resistance to movement through it, even though no eddies are formed to produce a wake which the body leaves behind. In this case the resistance is due to the fact that the fluid adheres to the surface of the body and in viscous substances a force is required to maintain a difference of velocity between contiguous layers. The force is of similar nature to one of friction. It tends to bring layers of fluid in contact with each other, to mutual rest. The energy which it dissipates is converted into heat in the fluid. Motion on the large scale is dominated by inertial effects, energy being carried away in the form of eddies in the way we have discussed. On the small scale, however, movement tends to be dominated by viscosity. The transition between the two states was studied by Osborne Reynolds.

Osborne Reynolds examined the conditions under which fluid motion would be similar in two cases in which the geometry of the boundaries was similar. His results are thus of the greatest importance in the consideration of experiments on models and in scaling up the results. The deduction of Reynolds' number, as it is called, is placed in Appendix VI. Reynolds' number is the name given to the quantity

$$R = \frac{\rho v l}{\mu} \qquad . \qquad . \qquad . \qquad . \qquad . \qquad 37$$

In this expression ρ is the density of the fluid, v is the fluid velocity, l is a length giving the dimension of an experiment and μ is the coefficient of viscosity of the fluid. The purpose of Reynolds' number is to determine when the fluid-flow in two like cases but of different scales, will be similar. This will be the case if Reynolds' number is the same for the two cases. Thus if ρ_1, v_1, l_1, and μ_1 refer to the first case and ρ_2, v_2, l_2, and μ_2 to the second, the flow will be similar if

$$\frac{\rho_1, v_1, l_1}{\mu_1} = \frac{\rho_2, v_2, l_2}{\mu_2}$$

This may make it clear that the particular velocities and lengths chosen to characterize each motion are unimportant, so long as corresponding values are selected. It is the ratio of the two sets of values which determines whether or not the motion will be similar.

Reynolds' number also provides a clue to the nature of a fluid motion by itself. A low value signifies that viscosity plays the dominant role, whereas when Reynolds' number is high, the inertial forces predominate. Reynolds' number will be small when the velocities and dimensions involved are small, or when the viscosity is high. This will be the case, for example, in the movement of protozoa, the action of cilia and similar small-scale phenomena. Inertia of the fluid will be of small importance compared to the forces caused by viscosity. At the other end of the scale, with the movement of large bodies through liquids, the inertial forces predominate and viscous forces are less important. Strictly speaking, it is only when it is arranged that Reynolds' number is unaltered that comparison between two cases can be made. The cases are then similar both geometrically and dynamically.

According to simple mechanics, the momentum contained in a cylinder of fluid one square centimetre in cross-section and v centimetres long, travelling with velocity v centimetres per second, will be ρv^2. This will impinge upon one square centimetre of a body placed at right angles to it in one second, and if it is brought to rest, a force equal to the rate of change of momentum will be exerted. This, in such a case, will clearly be ρv^2. Upon an area A square centimetres at right angles to the flow, the force would be $\rho A v^2$. This simple theory is inadequate for detailed calculation, which must take account of pressures set up as fluid flows round an object, but it is sufficient to give comparative results for the forces of inertia in two cases which are dynamically similar. Thus, if Reynolds' number is the same in two geometrically similar examples, the forces experienced will be proportional to $\rho A v^2$. This enables measurements made upon models to be applied to the full-scale cases. There is, however, one caveat which is very important. Our considerations so far have neglected energy losses occasioned by the generation of surface waves. Loss of energy because of wave formation is the predominant factor in determining the resistance experienced by ships moving on the surface, and a different law of similarity (Froude's law) is applied in their case. The foregoing considerations involving Reynolds' number apply to the motion of bodies entirely immersed in fluid and unable to generate surface waves.

APPENDIX VI

Considerations which lead to Reynolds' number are as follows. Reynolds' work is based upon securing that the ratio of the inertial to the frictional forces is the same in the two cases being compared. When this is achieved dynamical as well as geometrical similarity is said to be secured and the two fluid motions are similar.

As fluid flows along the streamlines, particles will go from a place where the velocity has a certain value to another where it is increased by, say, w centimetres per second. If these places are s centimetres apart and the average velocity in covering this distance is u, the particles will take $\dfrac{s}{u}$ seconds to cover the distance. That is, their velocity will increase by w centimetres per second every $\dfrac{s}{u}$ seconds. The acceleration will thus be $\dfrac{u \cdot w}{s}$ centimetres per second per second. If we consider unit volume, its mass will be ρ grams (ρ being the density of the fluid) so that the force on the fluid per unit volume necessary to overcome its inertia, will be

$$\frac{\rho u w}{s}$$

In going from the first case to the second, the ratio of all corresponding velocities and lengths will be the same when similarity is achieved. If, therefore, v is a specimen velocity and l a specimen length, we shall have the inertial forces proportional to

$$F_i = \frac{\rho v^2}{l}$$

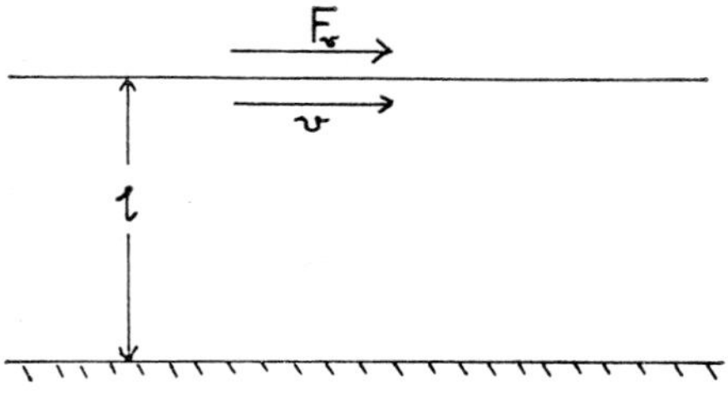

FIG. 129.

If a fluid has a coefficient of viscosity μ, then it requires a tangential force on every square centimetre equal to μ to maintain a velocity of one centimetre per second in a layer distant one centimetre from a layer at rest (Fig. 129). If a velocity v centimetres per second is maintained at a distance l centimetres from the layer at rest, the tangential force per unit area will be $\dfrac{\mu \cdot v}{l}$. This force will thus act on a volume one square centimetre by l centimetres, that is, on l cubic centimetres. The force per unit volume will be, therefore,

$$F_v = \frac{\mu \cdot v}{l^2}$$

The ratio of F_i to F_v will be

$$\frac{F_i}{F_v} = \frac{\rho l v}{\mu} = R$$

which is Reynolds' number.

Thus we see that when Reynolds' number is the same for the two cases being compared, the ratio of the inertial to the viscous forces is the same in the two cases, as was stated above, and the motions of the fluids are similar.

CHAPTER XVI

Interference, Diffraction and Group Velocity

THE properties possessed by waves on water have inspired investigations in many other branches of physics. Analogies with waves have been worked out in great detail in optics, sound and electricity, and these have become so familiar that we are accustomed to speak of light waves, sound waves or electromagnetic waves, without recalling the origin of the terms. Robert Hooke (1635–1703), who was assistant to Robert Boyle and later became Secretary to the Royal Society, and who played a considerable part in directing attention to the wave theory of light, wrote in his *Micrographia* in 1667, '. . . in an homogeneous medium this motion [i.e. light] is propagated in every way with equal velocity, whence necessarily every pulse or vibration of the luminous body will generate a sphere, which will continually increase, and grow bigger, just after the same manner (though indefinitely swifter) as the waves or rings on the surface of the water do swell into bigger and bigger circles about a point of it, where by the sinking of a stone the motion was begun . . .' This cross-fertilization has been most fruitful, and reactions from other branches have, in turn, helped the study of water waves forward. There is, for example, a close correspondence between the theory of vortices and electrodynamics, and some of the results in this field of hydrodynamics were first obtained in the course of studies in electrical theory. The interference of waves is another case in point. Because of its crucial importance in attempting to distinguish between wave and particle theories of light, the consequences of the interference of waves was fully investigated in optics. That two sources of light could, in places illuminated by both, produce darkness, appeared so paradoxical on any but a wave theory that it was taken as an indisputable indication of the wave nature of light. It would enlarge the scope of this book too much to consider, even superficially, waves other than those on water, and the reason for mentioning the other fields in which wavelike properties have been observed is only to be able to make use of some of the results in connection with water waves.

The basic principle which has been employed in the study of interference is that known under the name of the principle of superposition. This is the assumption that when two or more trains of waves are being generated their effect at any point will be obtained simply by adding the displacements caused by each wave separately. We have already employed this principle in studying standing waves (as in clapotis or the resonance of the water in gulfs) which are caused by the interference of two equal trains of waves (one of which is usually the reflection of the other) travelling in opposite directions. The principle is of wide application, but nevertheless, as we have seen, there are limitations which should be noticed. A wave is able to be propagated because particles displaced from their position at rest tend to return to it under the influence of a force occasioned by the displacement. If the force is proportional to the displacement, then clearly the force produced by the sum of the displacements caused by two waves, will be the sum of the forces which occur in the individual waves separately. The two waves will travel independently of each other. The resultant wave will be simply the 'sum' of the individual waves. If, however, the force were proportional to the square of the displacement, or if the expression for it contained terms involving the square or higher powers of the displacement, this would no longer be so. $(2x)^2$ is not equal to $2x^2$, and the two waves would not simply add up, and travel independently of each other. When the amplitude is small, terms involving squares and higher powers of the displacement are smaller still and can be neglected to a first approximation, and it so happens that in nature these terms are negligible in many cases. Nevertheless, there is a limit to the principle of superposition and also to the converse process of the analysis of waves into their Fourier constituents. While any curve can be looked upon as the sum of a number of simple harmonic curves, unless the equations of motion are linear, waves represented by these curves will not travel independently of one another. Having put in this caveat, however, we shall restrict ourselves to the consideration of cases where the principle of superposition can be applied.

Diffraction is the term applied to the bending of waves round obstacles, so that wave energy is propagated to points lying within geometrical shadows. This is of importance in considering the passage of waves behind breakwaters or through narrow openings into harbours. It can conveniently be studied in a ripple tank. Plates 36 and 37 show photographs of waves passing through openings in an obstacle in such a tank.

What happens when waves pass through an opening between breakwaters, depends upon the ratio of the width of the opening to the wavelength of the waves. When the opening is wide compared to the wavelength, as in Fig. 130, the waves tend to pass straight through, diffusing only slightly outwards as they proceed. With waves of long wavelength compared to the width of the opening, however, the behaviour is different. They tend to spread out in all directions as circular waves centred on the opening. In the first case the amplitude of the wave decreases only slightly in the forward direction, whereas in the second the

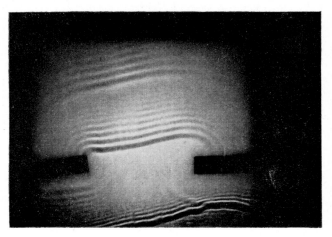

PLATE 36.—*Ripple tank photograph showing the passage of waves through an opening large compared with the wavelength. Except at the edges the waves travel straight forwards.*

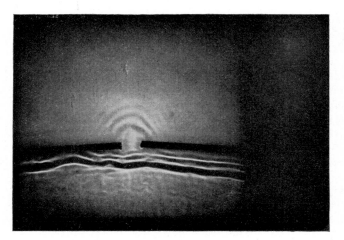

PLATE 37.—*Ripple tank photograph of waves passing through an opening which is small compared with the wavelength. Most of the wave is reflected and that which penetrates is of much less amplitude and spreads out in all directions.*

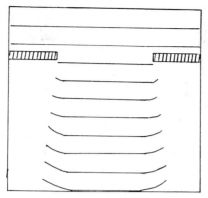

FIG. 130.

energy is spread almost evenly over the entire semicircle and the amplitude decreases more rapidly in all directions as we proceed farther from
the opening. With an opening of fixed size, as in an approach to a har-
bour, and with waves of different wavelength incident on the outside,
the short waves tend to travel straight on, corresponding to Fig. 130,
whereas the long waves spread out as in Fig. 131.

When two musical notes which are almost but not quite of the same
pitch are sounded together, a single note is heard which rises and falls
in intensity. The phenomenon is known as 'beats' in the sound and the
two sources of sound are said to beat together. If the pitch of one of the
sources of sound is variable the beats become slower and finally disappear entirely as the two sources are brought into tune with each

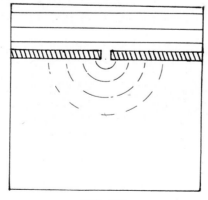

FIG. 131.

FIG. 132.

other, and, conversely, the beats become more frequent as the difference in frequency between the two sources is increased. The explanation of the phenomenon is simple. Suppose the sources of sound being used were two tuning forks and let us suppose that at a certain moment they are vibrating together; that is to say, the prongs of both advance towards the ear of the listener together. The sound waves which the two forks produce will reach the ear crest to crest and trough to trough, and so will produce an oscillation of twice the amplitude. (Sound waves are not in fact transverse displacements of the air like the transverse waves we have been studying on water, but the difference is unimportant in this connection.) However, after a time one of the forks will gain on the other so that when the prong of one advances that of the other will be retreating. The sound waves arrive at the ear, crest to trough and trough to crest, so that the resultant amplitude is a minimum. The resultant curve formed by adding together two sine curves of slightly different periods is shown in Fig. 132. Photographs of an apparatus for performing this addition mechanically are shown in Plate 38. It consists of a number of brass rods which can slide freely up and down in slots in the central bar of wood. Their lengths are cut so that when, as in the photo-

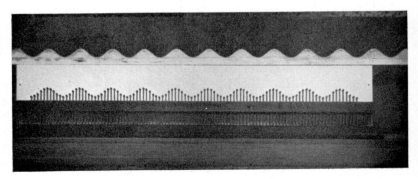

PLATE 38.—*Addition of wave motions. The brass rods in the lower part of the apparatus slide up and down in slots and their tops are cut so that they lie on a wave form. The piece of wood placed on the top of the apparatus is also cut to a wave form of the same amplitude and wavelength. This can be inserted underneath the brass rods as in the next picture.*

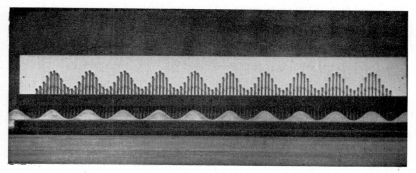

PLATE 39.—*The wave form on the wood, which was on the top of the apparatus in the last picture, has been placed under the brass rods, in such a position that the crests come under the crests on the rods themselves. The tops of the rods then indicate the sum of the two wave forms. A wave of double the amplitude of either wave singly results.*

graph, their lower ends rest on a level base, their tops trace out a sine curve. To render this curve more easily visible, the rods carry beads at their upper ends. On the top of the apparatus rests another sine curve cut out in wood, and this can be inserted underneath the rods so that their lower ends rest upon it. When this is done the upper ends of the rods receive a corresponding displacement, so that they then trace out the sum of the two curves. The wooden sine curve, in this case, is identical to that on the rods initially, so that the case illustrated would be the superposition of two equal trains of waves.

Plate 39 is a photograph of the apparatus with the wooden curve inserted underneath the rods. The two curves are arranged so that the

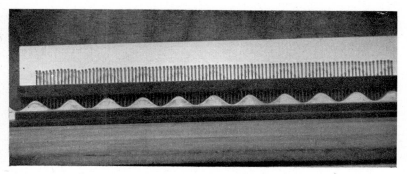

PLATE 40.—*In this picture the wave on the wood at the bottom has been moved along so that its crests fall under the troughs on the brass rods. The result, shown by the tops of the rods, is complete cancellation.*

crests and troughs of each coincide with those of the other and the upper ends of the rods display a curve of twice the amplitude of either component separately. Plate 40 shows the effect of placing the wooden curve so that its crests are opposite the troughs of the curve on the rods. The result is complete cancellation. The upper ends of the rods are all on a level.

In Plate 41 another wooden curve has been placed on the top of the apparatus. This curve has a slightly longer wavelength than that on the rods, so that while crest falls on crest at the left-hand side, farther to the right the crests on the upper curve coincide with troughs on the rods. In Plate 42 we see the effect of inserting this curve underneath the rods. When crest falls on crest, a large amplitude is produced in the

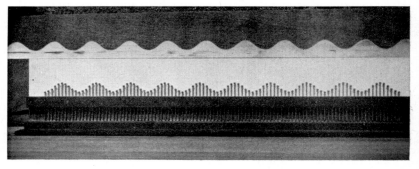

PLATE 41.—*Here a fresh wave on the wood has been placed on the top of the apparatus. In this case the wavelength on the wood is longer than that of the wave on the rods. On the left the crest of the wave on the wood coincides with the crests on the rods but in the middle the waves are out of phase and crests fall on troughs.*

curve at the top of the rods, but when crest falls on trough cancellation obtains. This is the case which gives rise to beats in sound, discussed in a previous paragraph.

Returning to the example of the tuning forks, if the frequency of one was greater than that of the other by, say, five, then it would gain a complete oscillation on the other one five times every second. There will thus be five beats per second. The number of beats heard per second is, in fact, equal to the difference in frequency between the two sources of sound producing them. Instruments are tuned together, in many cases, by listening to the beat frequency and adjusting the pitch of one until the beats disappear. The beats between the strings of one note on a piano are very noticeable if they are not quite in tune.

In the case of waves on water we do not come across two separate sources of waves of nearly the same frequency, except perhaps in the ripple tank specially set up to demonstrate the formation of beats, but nevertheless it has already been noticed that sea waves tend to vary rhythmically in amplitude in a similar manner. Groups of waves of large amplitude are separated by waves of small amplitude. These are the intermittent lulls between the groups of large waves which swimmers, small boats and, in rough seas, lifeboats, take advantage of to reach the beach or get into shelter. The propagation of groups of waves of this nature shows an important phenomenon which we have already touched upon and must now discuss more fully. We shall make use of it when studying the pattern of waves set up in a ship's wake, and it is of considerable theoretical importance in the propagation of other types of waves also. It occurs in all cases where the velocity of propagation of

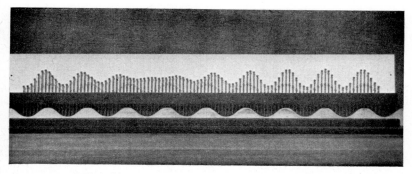

PLATE 42.—*When this wave is inserted under the brass rods there is cancellation in some places, where crest of one falls on the trough of the other, and at other places there is reinforcement, when crests and troughs coincide. The result is to form groups of waves separated by intervals of 'level water'.*

waves depends upon the wavelength, or, as it is sometimes expressed, where there is dispersion—a term borrowed from light where it is used to refer to the separation of the various colours of the spectrum by the passage of light through media in which waves of different wavelength travel with different velocities. Sound waves and electromagnetic waves in free space all travel with the same velocity whatever their wavelength, and dispersion does not occur.

If, as we might indeed expect, waves on water do not consist of pure sine waves of constant amplitude, but of a mixture of wavelengths all about the same size, then the various component trains would beat together and produce variations in amplitude similar to those of the two sound waves in Fig. 132. We would expect this to be the case since, although waves from a distant storm arrive at different times according to their wavelengths, the separation will not be complete. Waves of a certain wavelength will arrive at the same time as rather shorter waves which have spent longer on the journey but which set out from the storm area rather earlier. Had we been considering the case of the sound waves, both the components of slightly different wavelength would travel forward with the same velocity, so that the displacements depicted in Fig. 139 would be propagated through space as a whole. With gravity waves on deep water, however, the two components would travel at different speeds since their wavelengths are not quite the same, and so the pattern changes slowly as it proceeds. It is this change in the pattern which we must now investigate.

Let us draw, as in Fig. 133, the two waves separately which, when added together, produce a curve of beats as in Fig. 132. The one with the longer wavelength is drawn in the lower curve and the shorter one above it. At point A crest falls on crest, and at this position the resultant amplitude will be a maximum. At C, the two waves have got out of

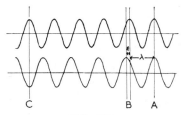

FIG. 133.

step, the crest of one falls on the trough of the other, so that the amplitude of the resultant displacement will be a minimum. Let us call the wavelength of the shorter wave λ and that of the longer $\lambda + \varepsilon$. Let us call the velocity with which the shorter wave is propagated, V. The longer wave will travel faster. Let us call its velocity of propagation $V + v$. The longer wave will, therefore, overtake the shorter with a relative velocity v. It will pick up a distance ε in a time $t = \dfrac{\varepsilon}{v}$. In this time, therefore, the crest of the long wave near B will have overtaken the corresponding crest of the short wave. The two waves will then be crest to crest at B instead of A and the position of maximum amplitude in the resultant wave will have fallen back from A to B. The maximum in the resultant amplitude will thus fall back a distance λ in a time t seconds, that is, it will drop back at a speed $\dfrac{\lambda v}{\varepsilon}$, relative to the waves.

Now the velocity of the short waves will be given by

$$V^2 = \frac{\lambda g}{2\pi}$$

PLATE XX.—*Reflections of the sky. The high-lights tend to produce obvious reflections whereas the darker parts get lost.*

and that of the long wave by

$$(V + v)^2 = \frac{(\lambda + \varepsilon)g}{2\pi}$$

so that

$$(V + v)^2 - V^2 = \frac{\varepsilon g}{2\pi}$$

or

$$(2V + v)v = \frac{\varepsilon g}{2\pi}$$

If the waves are nearly of the same wavelength, as they would have to be if they are to produce beats which are at all obvious, they will travel at nearly the same speed. Thus v will be small compared with V and will make little difference when added to $2V$ in the bracket, on the left-hand side of this equation.

Neglecting v inside this bracket we obtain

$$\frac{v}{\varepsilon} = \frac{g}{4\pi V}$$

The point of maximum amplitude, therefore, falls back with a velocity relative to the waves given approximately by

$$\frac{\lambda v}{\varepsilon} = \frac{\lambda g}{4\pi V}$$

But

$$\frac{\lambda g}{2\pi} = V^2$$

so that the velocity with which the point of maximum amplitude falls back, relative to the waves, $\dfrac{\lambda v}{\varepsilon}$ will be $\dfrac{V}{2}$.

The waves travel forward with a velocity V so that the maximum amplitude travels forward with a velocity

$$V_g = V - \frac{V}{2} = \frac{V}{2}$$

The velocity V_g is known as the group velocity. The group of gravity waves on deep water travels forward with only half the velocity of the waves. Thus crests of small amplitude at the back of a group pass forward through it. They grow in amplitude as they do so until they reach the point of maximum amplitude in the middle. After passing this point they then decrease in amplitude until they pass out of the front of the group as crests of small amplitude. After that they then overtake the group in front and are propagated in the same manner through it. Waves, therefore, are continually forming at the back of a group, passing forward through it as it travels along, and dying away in front.

o

This phenomenon of wave groups and group velocity is a most interesting and important property. Lord Rayleigh first pointed out that the
energy transported by waves must travel with the group rather than the
wave velocity. When we calculated the distance of a storm from considerations of the gradual change in wavelength of the waves striking
the shore, it was the group velocity rather than the wave velocity which
had to be employed. Could we have followed an individual wave from
the storm, we would have seen it pass from group to group, overtaking
one after another and finally arriving at the front of the train where the
groups themselves would gradually diminish and finally merge into the
undisturbed water in front. The wave which we were following would,
therefore, gradually have died out as it overtook the front of the disturbance arising from the storm, and it would never have arrived at our
wave recorder. It is interesting to think that the actual crests and troughs
registered by the recorder formed a comparatively short distance away,
at the back of the train of waves coming from the storm, although they
were, in fact, generated from energy put into the water by the storm at
a much greater distance.

The phenomenon of group velocity is not at all difficult to see if one
knows where to look for it. It does not occur very obviously in any of
the places which one would naturally tend to investigate at first sight.
It does not occur with waves in shallow water, for example. The velocity
of propagation of waves in shallow water is $\sqrt{gD}$ and is the same for all
wavelengths. It is, therefore, quite useless to expect to see it in waves
approaching a shelving beach. To make matters more difficult the height
of waves increases as they approach such a beach. The process is not by
any means uniform. Waves peak up, and often break, as they pass over
shallower patches, and reform with less amplitude if there is deeper
water closer in shore. It is virtually impossible to see anything of the
phenomenon from the beach. On the other hand, if one goes out on to a
breakwater and looks over deeper water, in an attempt to see the phenomenon there, the task is again rendered well-nigh impossible by the
waves reflected off the breakwater wall. Breakwaters, also, are not often
built in water which is sufficiently deep, and the groups of waves in an
ordinary sea are too long for the point of maximum amplitude to be
readily identified and followed for sufficient time. The same is true of
attempts to see the propagation of wave groups from a ship at sea, and,
in this case, the platform from which observation is being made is
moving to boot.

The writer has frequently been told that the phenomenon can readily
be seen when a stone is thrown into a pond. Having thrown innumer-
able stones into many pieces of water without ever having been able to
see what he has been looking for, he does not recommend the process

for easily demonstrating the effect. It is clear that the longer waves produced in this way (Plate 43) travel more quickly than the shorter, and in consequence the ring of waves grows with the longest on the outside. It is true that it follows from this that the phenomenon—of the group velocity being less than the wave velocity—must occur, but it is not possible to follow an individual wave and watch it being propagated through a group, see it grow to a maximum and then diminish. At any rate, the writer has never succeeded in doing so in spite of attempts spread over many years.

PLATE 43.—*Waves produced by a stone thrown into a pond. The waves of short wavelength travel more slowly than the long waves. Therefore, the short waves are to be found on the inside of the circle with the long ones on the outside.*

Instead, he would recommend those who wish to see this happening to watch waves on a reservoir, lake or loch, when fairly fresh winds raise good waves, with an occasional one breaking. The waves so produced travel in small well-defined groups of six or seven waves apiece. Their wavelength is short enough for several whole groups to be observed at once, and they can be watched satisfactorily from the bank, because, although the water nearby is shallow, short waves, such as occur on a reservoir, do not require any great depth for their behaviour to correspond to that of waves on deep water. They are, nevertheless, sufficiently longer in wavelength than pure ripples, which behave differently, as we shall see in Chapter XVIII. A short time spent in watching

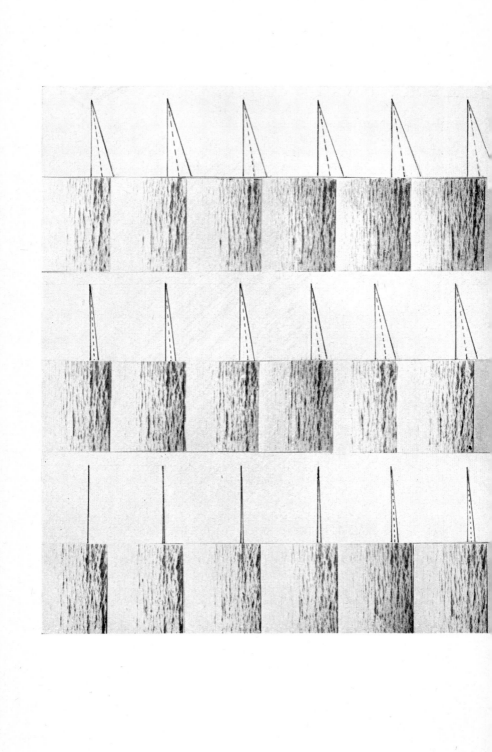

reservoir waves will enable all the phenomena associated with the propagation of wave groups to be clearly seen. Pick out first of all a large wave in a group approaching. In a very short time it will be the next wave following which will take over the office of largest of the group, and a short time later the one following that, and so on. Conversely, by watching an individual wave instead of a group, it can be followed as it grows while overtaking the centre of a group, then diminishes as it passes this point and finally becomes quite small as it passes out of the group in front. It is often possible to continue to follow its progress as it enters the group in front, and grows again only to diminish once more as it gains the front of that group in turn.

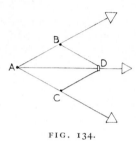

FIG. 134.

Plate 44 shows shots from a film of waves on a reservoir. Every fourth picture only is reproduced, as the change between consecutive pictures is too small to be readily noticeable and it is impossible, in any case, to reproduce a sufficient length of film on a page in a book if every picture is included. A conspicuous wave in the first picture is marked by the horizontal line which remains in the same position on all the following pictures. The lower, continuous line is drawn to mark the position of the wave as it advances towards the camera. After the wave has passed out of the picture the lower line is advanced at the same rate as previously so that it continues to point to the position which the wave occupies. The dotted line bisects the angle between the first two lines and it is seen to point to the position of maximum amplitude of the group. It thus furnishes a rough confirmation of the calculation that the group velocity of these waves is half the wave velocity. With the ciné film running this fact can be verified more convincingly since it is possible

PLATE 44.—*Group velocity. Pictures of waves on a reservoir, taken from a ciné film. The upper line marks the initial position of a wave of large amplitude. The lower line follows this wave along. As it travels, however, its amplitude decreases while that of the wave behind grows. It is seen that the place of maximum amplitude follows the dotted line very nearly. The dotted line bisects the angle between the other two lines, showing that the group velocity is about half the wave velocity.*

to follow the progress of a group for longer. A pair of three-legged cali-
pers is constructed, according to the diagram of Fig. 134. The three
arms are hinged together at A and the centre arm is fixed by means of
two smaller arms, BD and DC, hinged at B and C and fastened to a ring
at D, which slides along the centre arm. The centre arm is thus always
midway between the two other arms. Observation starts with the arms
closed together and the pointers placed against a conspicuous wave in
the ciné picture on the screen. The top pointer is held stationary in this
position while the wave is followed with the lower arm. When this is
done it is found that the centre arm always points to the position in the
train of waves where the amplitude is a maximum. Since the change in
the depression of the line of sight below the horizontal remains small
throughout the sequence of pictures, this procedure shows clearly that
the group velocity (or the velocity of the point of maximum amplitude)
is about half the velocity of the waves themselves.

CHAPTER XVII

Ships' Wakes

WHEN a ship travels through water, energy has to be supplied to overcome the viscous resistance of the water, to stir up the water in the
eddies in its turbulent wake, and to generate on the surface a system of
waves which travel along with the vessel and continually extend the
area over which they occur. The most important drain on the energy
of the ship is this system of waves, and it is to them that most attention
must be given if any significant reduction in the power required to drive
a vessel forwards is sought. We have already discussed one example of
this in the case of canal boats and the 'discovery' made by Mr Houston's
horse. Moreover, the pattern of waves set up when a body moves along
the surface of water is an intriguing natural phenomenon which we meet
almost every time we come across a pond or stream. The essential
features of the wave pattern formed by ships are to be seen in miniature
whenever a duck or moorhen exerts itself to any extent, and a search
through the photograph album of most families will reveal an example or
two of these waves. Plate 45 and Colour Plates XI–XIV are illustrations.

There are three main features which may easily be seen in the wake
of a ship sailing in deep water, or of water birds in water which is deep
compared with the wavelength of the wavelets they generate. The most
conspicuous are the two lines of waves which spread out from the front
of the object, where they meet at an angle, as in Fig. 135. One would
naturally assume that this angle would vary with the speed of the boat,
being small when the vessel is travelling rapidly and large when it is
travelling slowly. Paradoxical as it may appear, however, this is not so.
So long as the boat is travelling in water which is deep compared to the
wavelength of the waves it is producing, the angle remains the same.
It is, in fact, always 39°.

A closer inspection of these lines of waves will reveal that they are
not made up of a single wave but are composed of a number of short
waves. These waves are not arranged parallel to the two lines emanating
from the bows but are inclined at a certain angle to them. These component waves travel forwards through the lines from the bows, at the
same time as they travel outwards with them, as the lines get gradually
farther and farther apart. This is also indicated in Fig. 135.

Finally, directly astern of the vessel is another series of waves which
travels forward at the same speed as the vessel does itself, keeping
station with it. Their wavelength is longer than that of the waves in the

201

FIG. 135.

side trains. They are a conspicuous feature in the seascape looking out over the stern of a steamer, and it is not difficult to realize that a considerable part of the work done by the engines of the ship has gone to generate this system of waves tailing along behind and extending almost as far as eye can see.

The pattern of waves set up by a ship on the surface of the sea was investigated by Lord Kelvin. His principal paper on this subject appeared in the proceedings of the Royal Society of Edinburgh for June 20th 1904, and in volume IX of the *Philosophical Magazine* of June 1905. But he had referred to the subject much earlier (proceedings of the Institute of Mechanical Engineers, August 3rd 1887; *Popular Lectures*, volume 3, page 482) where he mentions a method based on the theory of group velocity. Kelvin's mathematical investigation is far too difficult for this book and his method based on group velocity has, unfortunately, never been published. It is possible that the simple discussion of the problem which follows, may be on similar lines, but there is no means of verifying whether or not it is so.

Suppose a ship travels from O to P (Fig. 136) with uniform speed, and let us take as our unit of time, the time it takes to do so. OP will then represent the velocity of the ship in these units. Suppose, when it was at O, it generated a wave of such a wavelength that its wave velocity would be represented by OR. By the time the ship had reached P this wave, which it had generated at O, would have spread out into a circle of radius OR, as shown in Fig. 136. Similarly, the wave of the same wavelength and velocity, which it generated at each other point of its path, such as M, would also have spread out into circles, the radii of which would be proportional to the time the ship takes to go from M to P. These particular waves, if they were continually being generated at all points on the ship's course, would reinforce along the common tangent to these circles—for similar reasons to those underlying Huyghens' construction for the wavefront.

A ship may be expected to generate a wide range of wavelengths as it travels through the water, just as a stone does when thrown into a pond. The water is heaped up in front of the bows and then oscillates as it falls back as the ship passes, just as the water does in the case of the stone thrown into the pond. In forming the wake which follows a ship, however, only those waves which possess the right wavelength, so that they are able to keep station with the ship, will be important. If the ship continues to generate wavelets at each point of its track as it passes

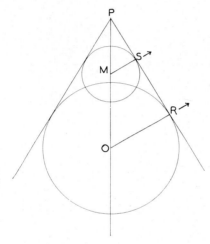

FIG. 136.

along, those wavelets which are of the right speed and in the right position to reinforce each other, crest falling on crest and trough on trough, alone will contribute significantly to the visible wake. Other wavelets which travel too fast will be propagated away and those which travel too slowly will be left behind. If this view is correct, the pattern of the waves which forms the wake of a vessel, and which travels along as if attached to it, will be produced by mutual reinforcement of a large number of small components generated as the ship moves along.

Since the wavefront PR corresponding to waves of a particular velocity generated by the ship, will be at right angles to OR (the radius of the contributory wavelet from O), PRO must lie in a semicircle drawn on PO (Fig. 137). Now PR is the wavefront of waves generated as the ship passes along OP, which are able to keep pace with her while

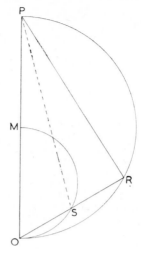

FIG. 137.

they travel in the direction of *OR*. The energy which these waves contain, however, will travel with the group velocity, which is only half the velocity of the waves, and will, therefore, be found along the line *PS* (*OS* = *SR*).

Similarly, waves propagated with the appropriate wavelength and

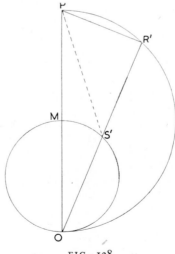

FIG. 138.

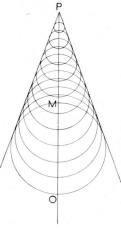

FIG. 139.

velocity in other directions from O, such as OR' (Fig. 138), will have their energy at the half-way point S'. Thus the energy of all the waves generated at O and which possess the velocity appropriate to their direction to enable them to maintain station with the ship, will lie on the small circle drawn on MO as diameter, as in Fig. 138. The energy of the waves of the wake will, therefore, be concentrated along the envelope of all these small circles, such as that on MO, drawn for all points along the course of the vessel. This envelope will be the common

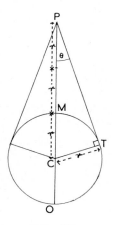

FIG. 140.

tangent to all these circles drawn from P, as in Fig. 139. The part of the wake of a vessel formed by waves travelling obliquely to its path would be expected, therefore, to be concentrated upon the lines of these two common tangents.

We have thus seen how one of the principal characteristics of a ship's wake may originate, for the angle between these two tangents is independent of the ship's speed. The circles to which these tangents are drawn must not be confused with circular wavelets spreading out from each point of the track. They have been constructed for each point of the course by drawing them on half the line from the point to the present position of the ship, as diameter. We may easily calculate the angle between the two legs of this part of a ship's wake.

Referring to Fig. 140, MO is, as before, half OP. The radius of the circle on MO as diameter is half MO. If we call this radius r, CP will be $3r$ in length and CT will, of course, be equal to r. Thus the sine of θ, the semi-apical angle of the wake, will be

$$\text{sine } \theta = \tfrac{1}{3}$$

This makes
$$\theta = 19° \, 28'$$

and the angle between the two arms of the wake

$$2\theta = 39° \text{ very nearly}$$

It is the same at whatever speed the ship proceeds.

The wavefront of the waves in these side arms of the wake will not be parallel to the arms themselves—that is, they will not be parallel to PT in Fig. 141. The waves at T were generated when the ship was at O and the wavefronts will be at right angles to OT and thus parallel to MT.

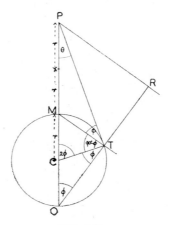

FIG. 141.

PLATE 45.—*The wake generated by a swan.*

Had the waves not fallen back, because of the effect of group velocity, they would have attained the position *PR*. Suppose the waves cross the line of the wake at an angle ϕ. The angle *MTP* will thus equal ϕ and the angle *MTC* will equal $90° - \phi$, so that the angle *CTO* (and hence also *COT*) will equal ϕ. The angle *MCT* equals 2ϕ, therefore, and

$$2\phi = 90° - \theta$$
$$= 90° - 19° \, 29'$$
$$= 70° \, 31'$$

thus $\phi = 35° \, 15'$

and this is the angle between the lines of the arms of the wake and the wavefronts which form them.

This part of the simple theory of wakes accounts qualitatively for the general appearance of the side arms and provides two angles by which it can be compared quantitatively with observation. The angles ϕ and θ may be measured on photographs of ships' wakes taken from vertically overhead, and the theoretical values compared with those observed. Plate 46 is an aerial photograph of German mine-sweepers at work during the last war. A paper triangle possessing angles of $39°$ and $109\frac{1}{2}°$ may easily be constructed and can be used to measure the angles in the photograph.

The remaining part of the wake of a ship comprises the waves which

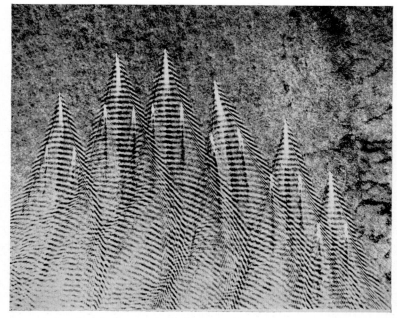

PLATE 46.—*Aerial photograph of German mine-sweepers at work. The angles formed by the waves in the wakes may be measured by means of a cardboard triangle (see p. 207). The angle of 39° will be found to agree with the angle between the two arms of the wakes and that of 109½° with the angle between the waves in the arms of a wake. (By courtesy of the Imperial War Museum.)*

follow her behind and travel in the same direction as that in which she is going. They are of such a wavelength that they travel at the same speed as the ship. If the speed of the ship is known and the wavelength of the waves can be measured from an aerial photograph, it is possible to check that the velocity of the waves and the ship are the same, by means of the relation

$$c = \sqrt{\frac{\lambda g}{2\pi}}$$

As a rule, however, the speed of the ship would not be known at the time a photograph is taken, independently of determining it from the wavelength of the waves it sets up. There is, nevertheless, one other measurement which can be made solely on the photograph, which enables the theory to be checked. This is the ratio of the wavelengths of the waves forming the lateral arms of the wake and that of the waves following the ship astern.

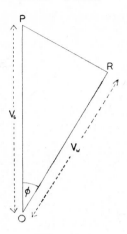

FIG. 142.

The relevant parts of the previous figures are reproduced in Fig. 142. The waves astern travel in the direction OP with a velocity equal to that of the ship, V_s. We represented this velocity by the line OP. On the same scale the velocity of the waves in the lateral arms of the wake will be represented by OR. Calling the velocity of the waves in the arms V_w, we see from Fig. 142 that

$$\frac{V_w}{V_s} = \cos\phi$$

If λ_w and λ_s are the wavelengths of the lateral waves and those astern respectively,

$$V_w = \sqrt{\frac{\lambda_w g}{2\pi}}$$

and

$$V_s = \sqrt{\frac{\lambda_s g}{2\pi}}$$

so that

$$\frac{\lambda_w}{\lambda_s} = \frac{V_w{}^2}{V_s{}^2} = \cos^2\phi$$

Either from tables, or from the fact that

$$\cos^2\phi = \frac{1 + \cos 2\phi}{2}$$

$$= \frac{1 + \sin\theta}{2}$$

we see that the ratio of the wavelengths of the two sets of waves is

$$\frac{\lambda_w}{\lambda_s} = \tfrac{2}{3}$$

This ratio may be determined from photographs by direct measurement.

The full facts provided by this simple theory, which are well confirmed by experiment, may be summarized diagrammatically as in Fig. 143.

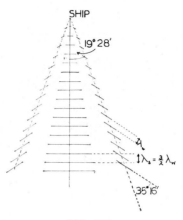

FIG. 143.

What we have discussed so far is really the wave pattern which would be set up by some pressure disturbance following the course of the ship. We have not considered the ship's length or the waves generated by various parts of her hull. The pattern, though essentially as is given in Fig. 143, varies considerably in other characteristics, such as in the amplitude of the waves, with changes in the dimensions of the vessel. To a first approximation, a train of waves like those indicated in Fig. 143 is set up by the bows, and another by the stern. The two trains interfere. The speed of the vessel adjusts itself until the output from the engines which is left over after the viscous drag and the eddy resistance have been overcome, is just sufficient to counterbalance the energy dissipated in the waves of the wake.

Since in deep water the group velocity of the waves is one-half that of the waves themselves, the part of the wake following astern the ship extends back from the vessel at a relative speed equal to half that of the ship. The wake, therefore, extends backwards from the ship for half the distance that the latter has travelled. This applies only within limits, of course, and as the tail of the wake gets farther and farther behind, more and more of the energy supplied by the ship is dissipated before it reaches the end of the wake. Waves are, however, propagated to great distances and anyone who has seen the sea from an aeroplane will have noticed the length of wake which is to be found behind the ships which are passed over. If it is possible to measure the wavelength of the waves which follow astern either from photographs or by other means, aerial reconnaissance can furnish knowledge of the speed at which ships are travelling.

W. Froude, who studied the wave-making resistance of ships, considered the question of the estimation of wave resistance from models. He worked on the assumption that the conditions in two geometrically similar cases would be similar, from the point of view of their wave dynamics, if corresponding lengths in the two vessels were in the same ratio as the lengths of the waves which were generated. If the subscripts referred to the two cases being compared, respectively, the velocities V and wavelengths λ would follow the relation

$$\frac{V_1{}^2}{V_2{}^2} = \frac{\lambda_1 g}{\lambda_2 g}$$

or if the wavelengths are to be proportional to the linear dimensions.

$$\frac{V_1{}^2}{l_1 g} = \frac{V_2{}^2}{l_2 g} \qquad . \qquad . \qquad . \qquad . \qquad 38$$

This is known as Froude's Law of corresponding speeds.

Since it is generally not possible to vary the acceleration of gravity, Froude's Law makes corresponding speeds proportional to the square roots of the linear dimensions. It will be recalled that Reynolds' number, the constancy of which ensures dynamical similarity in the two cases, makes the speeds inversely proportional to the lengths, so long as the density and viscosity of the fluid are the same in the two cases. It is thus not possible to satisfy the criteria of both Reynolds and Froude at the same time. Since it is the waves which are responsible for the bulk of the resistance to motion in the case of a ship, it is Froude's Law which is applied in the case of experiments with models of ships, rather than Reynolds' Law of similarity. This, of course, is appropriate only in cases of vessels proceeding on the surface. In the case of submarines or of calculations about the horse-power exerted by fish, for example, Froude's Law would not enter into the question.

Very occasionally, however, waves are generated by ships below the surface of the sea. This was thought to occur in the mouths of some of the Norwegian fjords where a layer of less dense fresh water overlays a layer of salt. The difference in density between the two layers is slight

P

and waves in the interface of considerable height would be easily produced. It was the generation of waves in the boundary to which Ekman ascribed (in a report on 'Dead Water' among the scientific results of a Polar expedition) the abnormal resistance sometimes said to be experienced by ships in these areas.

The characteristics of the wakes we have been discussing so far are to be seen only in water which is deep compared with the wavelengths of the waves of the wake. In these cases the energy of the waves is propagated at a velocity, the group velocity, which is significantly different from that of the waves. We have found that in deep water the group velocity is one-half the wave velocity, and it has been on the assumption that this relation holds true that our theory has been developed. The theory, therefore, can only be expected to be applicable to cases where the assumption that the water is deep, holds true. It has been mentioned in an earlier chapter that waves 'feel the bottom' when the water becomes less than half a wavelength deep, so that whether or not a particular case can be considered to be one of deep water will depend upon the wavelength of the waves forming the wake. Now the waves in the wake of a ship are of such wavelength that they are able to keep station with the ship. If the velocity of the ship approaches the velocity $\sqrt{gD}$, which long waves possess in the depth D of the water in which the ship is sailing, then the waves it generates will have the characteristics of shallow water waves, and the assumption of deep water will not hold. Thus we can expect to find the characteristics of the wakes we have been discussing so far, only in cases where the velocity of the body travelling across the surface of the water is small compared with $\sqrt{gD}$.

TABLE VII

Depth of water (fathoms)	1	2	4	8	12	16	25	50	100
Velocity of Long Waves ($\sqrt{gD}$)									
feet per second	14	19·7	29	39·2	48	54·3	69·3	98	139
miles per hour	9½	13½	20	24	33	37	47	62	95

Table VII gives the velocity of long waves in water of varying depths. Thus we might expect to find wakes showing fairly accurately the characteristics appropriate to deep water, in the case of a duck, for example, swimming in 6 feet of water at 2 or 3 miles per hour (which is fairly energetically for a duck), or by a motor-boat or small steamer travelling at 8 or so knots in 8 fathoms of water. A destroyer on the other hand, or speed boat, would require very deep water, of the order of 25 fathoms or more, before it could be expected to reproduce accurately the angles we have calculated for wakes in deep water. Qualitatively, however, the picture will remain substantially correct for velocities equal to, and even somewhat greater than, those occurring in Table VII.

Elementary considerations are adequate to deal with the case of wakes in shallow water where things are, indeed, very much simpler than those in deep water. To cover the intermediate field, however, we must content ourselves with qualitative observations directed by extrapolations from what we have been able to deduce for the two extreme cases of deep and shallow water respectively.

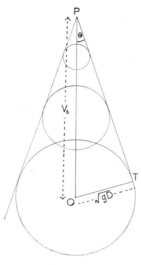

FIG. 144.

In shallow water waves of all wavelengths travel with the same velocity $\sqrt{gD}$. The group velocity is therefore also the same as the wave velocity. We would, therefore, expect to find a wake in which the apical angle varied with the speed of the vessel. Wavelets generated as the vessel passes through various points of its track will spread out with velocity $\sqrt{gD}$ irrespective of wavelength and will thus all lie on circles having a common tangent through P, the present position of the vessel (Fig. 144). The semi-apical angle of the wake, θ, will be given by

$$\sin \theta = \frac{\sqrt{gD}}{V_s}$$

Thus, as the speed of the vessel, V_s, increases, the angle θ becomes progressively smaller and smaller. The wavefronts of the wake lie along the line PT so that the angle which we have previously called ϕ between the wavefronts and the line of the wake, has become zero and the waves have lined themselves up parallel to the wake. Lastly, the speed of the vessel being greater than $\sqrt{gD}$, there is no wave which is capable of maintaining station astern the ship and following it in the same direction in which it is travelling. As was discovered in the case of Mr Houston's horse, the 'foaming stern surge which used to devastate the banks' of the canals, has disappeared.

An example of an intermediate case is furnished by the motor torpedo boat proceeding up the Seine, of which a photograph is reproduced in Colour Plate XII. The depth of the Seine at this point is of the order of 5 fathoms and, although the boat is travelling at a lower velocity than $\sqrt{gD}$ so that a 'stern surge' is clearly generated, the waves in the two lateral arms are obviously seen to be more nearly parallel to the arms themselves than would be the case in deep water, even though the photograph has been taken obliquely, so that it is not possible to measure the angles accurately.

This is about as far as we can take the theory of ships' wakes within the limitations of this book. We may summarize our results as follows. In deep water, or when the velocity of the vessel is small, the wake consists of two parts. One part comprises the two lines of waves spreading out from the ship at an angle of $19\frac{1}{2}°$ with the line of the ship's course, and the waves which form these lines cross them at an angle of $35\frac{1}{4}°$. The other part consists of waves travelling in the same direction as the ship and following it astern at the same speed. The wake extends for half the distance which the ship has travelled.

When the speed of the ship is high the waves following astern are no longer formed, in shallow water. The waves in the diverging lateral lines lie parallel to these lines and the angle which the wake makes with the course of the ship depends on the speed of the vessel, becoming smaller as the speed increases.

Between these two cases it is impossible to explore if we are restricted to elementary methods. We can only surmise that there must be a transition between the two. We have, however, been able to understand the cause of all the main features of the phenomenon of wave wakes and even to obtain accurate quantitative results in the two extreme cases into one or other of which most of those which occur in practice fall.

CHAPTER XVIII

Surface Tension

IN the case of all the waves on the surface of water with which we have been concerned so far, the agent responsible for their propagation has been gravity. The origin of the waves may have lain in other directions, such as the wind, but once formed it has been gravity which has been responsible for the fact that they have travelled forward and persisted while they did so. For this reason they are, in fact, known as gravity waves. As the wavelength of the waves diminishes another factor becomes important, however, and in the case of waves of only a few millimetres in length it predominates. This factor is surface tension, and, as a preliminary to the study of these tiny waves or ripples, we will spend a little time discussing the nature of this force.

When water drips from a tap it does not immediately fall away but hangs suspended in a drop, which looks curiously as though it is covered with a stretched skin. The drop itself is rounded in shape, and as it grows becomes attached to the tap by means of a narrow neck, which finally severs when the drop falls off. The shape of the hanging drop can be imitated very closely by pouring water into a rubber membrane such as a toy balloon. The water collects into a large rounded blob and above it there forms a distinct neck, reminiscent of the neck above the water drop hanging from the tap. The water in the rubber bag is supported by the forces set up in the rubber as it stretches, suggesting that the drop under the tap may be similarly supported by tensions in the surface of the water, which seems to behave as though it had a thin skin covering it. Plates 47 to 50 show the shape of a drop as it falls from a tube, while Plate 51 is a photograph of a rubber balloon filled with water, showing how its shape resembles that of a drop of liquid hanging from a tube.

The suggestion of a surface skin is reinforced by the fact that small, though dense, bodies, which would sink to the bottom if they are immersed in water and left to themselves, can be made to float on the surface skin. Plate 52 is a photograph of a sewing needle floating on the surface of water. Many aquatic insects avail themselves of this effect. Some, such as pond skaters and whirligig beetles, are able to support themselves above the surface of a pond or stream. Others, such as culex larvae (gnat larvae), hang from it underneath. In the case of culex larvae, their breathing tube is pushed through the skin so that the animal is able to breathe the air above the water while it hangs

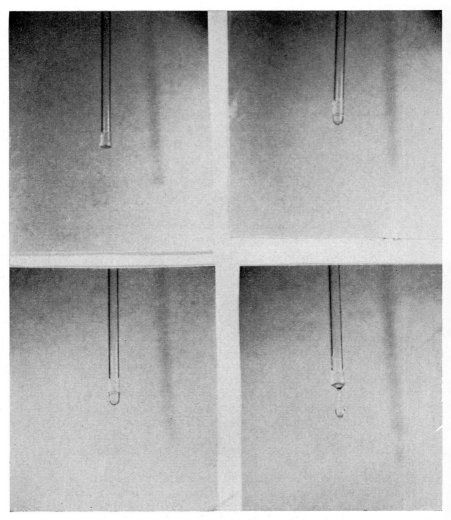

PLATES 47, 48, 49 and 50.—*Stages in the breaking away of a drop from the end of a tube. A neck forms above the drop which then breaks as the drop falls.*

PLATE 51.—*A rubber balloon filled with water. The tension in the rubber simulates that of the surface of water and the shape is similar to that of a drop on the end of a tube.*

suspended from the surface, in the water beneath, where it feeds on the micro-organisms in the liquid.

A closer examination of the floating needle will reveal that it rests in a small depression in the surface of the water, as in the diagram of Fig. 145. It is this depression which enables the tension of the surface to act in a direction inclined to the horizontal and thus to have a

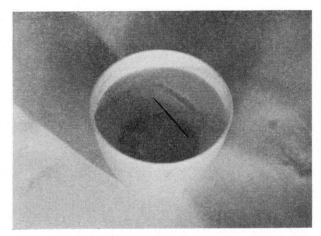

PLATE 52.—*A needle floating on the surface of water. The shadow of the depression in which the needle lies can be seen on the side of the cup.*

component force in the vertical direction, which can support the weight of the needle.

A further demonstration of the apparent tension in the surface of the liquid is provided by the shape of liquid drops. Small drops of liquid, such as rain drops, assume a spherical form. The sphere is the solid figure which possesses the least surface area for a given volume, so that it is the shape that a liquid might be expected to assume if its surface behaved as though it was covered by a skin in a state of tension. Larger drops become distorted by the weight of the liquid, but if this is compensated by forming the drop inside another liquid of the same density, then quite large drops can be seen to be spherical in shape if left to themselves. Plate 53 is a photograph of a drop of engine oil suspended in a mixture of alcohol and water, the composition of which has been adjusted to give the same density as that of the oil. Actually the drop

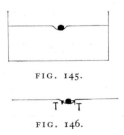

FIG. 145.

FIG. 146.

PLATE 53.—*A large drop of engine oil floating in a mixture of alcohol and water. It rests on a denser layer containing less alcohol at the bottom of the vessel and its shape is somewhat oblate.*

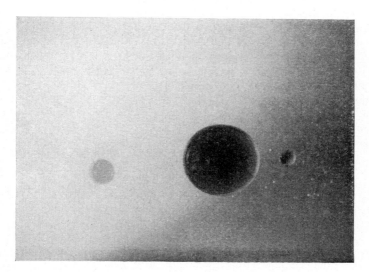

PLATE 54.—*The alcohol-water mixture has been adjusted to have the same density as the oil and the shape of the drop then becomes spherical, buoyancy counter-balancing the weight of the drop which is acted on only by its surface tension.*

rests upon a layer of liquid with a slightly greater density formed by mixing rather more water with the alcohol, above which is a layer of rather less dense liquid containing more alcohol. The weight of the oil drop is thus only partially counterbalanced by buoyancy in the less dense layer and the drop is somewhat oblate in form. The smaller drop close by, however, is almost perfectly spherical in shape. In Plate 54 the density of the drop is more nearly the same as that of the surrounding liquid and even the large drop then takes up a spherical shape.

Soap films, though made from a solution, and not therefore composed of pure water, also demonstrate the tension which can exist in the surface of liquids. Plates 55 and 56 show photographs of a soap film made across a rectangular frame of wire. In Plate 55 a length of cotton is tied across the frame. When the film is broken on one side of the cotton, the tension in the surface on the other side, which is no longer compensated by a similar tension when the film is broken, is clearly indicated by the circular shape taken up by the thread. In Plate 56 a loop of cotton thread has been placed on the film and the film broken inside it. In this case the loop assumes the form of a complete circle.

The tension in the soap film is not the same as in a surface of pure water. Surface tension is altered by the presence of substances in solution. Most substances dissolved in water reduce the surface tension. If a shallow layer of coloured water is placed in a white dish and a drop of alcohol allowed to fall in the middle, the water will be drawn away from the place where it falls. The surface tension of the water is reduced when the alcohol dissolves in it and the water is pulled away from the spot by the stronger tension in the remaining water. The movement of camphor on water can be explained in the same way, as can the formation of 'tears' in a wine glass. Plate 57 shows the effect of a drop of alcohol on a thin layer of coloured water in a flat white dish.

It is important for our purpose to understand how surface tension may be measured quantitatively, in addition to obtaining a qualitative idea of the apparent tension in liquid surfaces, by experiments similar to those described in the preceding paragraphs. The quantitative definition of surface tension may be most easily understood by considering a soap film on a wire frame (Fig. 147). The film is drawn held in position by a sliding wire, AB. To prevent the film from contracting, a force F has to be applied to it. A soap film has two surfaces, each of which is looked upon as contributing equally to the force the film exerts on AB. The force exerted on each centimetre length of the wire AB by one surface of the film, is known as its surface tension, T. Surface tension is thus measured as a force per unit length—in dynes per centimetre, when the centimetre-gramme-second system is used. The

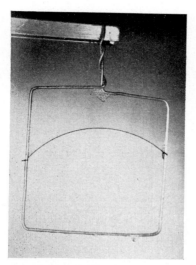

PLATE 55.—*Surface tension in a soap film. A soap film was formed across the wire frame across which a piece of cotton thread was tied. The film below the thread was broken and the tension in the film above stretched the thread into a circular arc.*

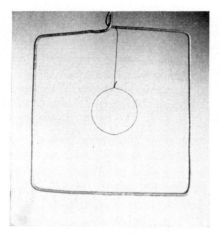

PLATE 56.—*Surface tension in a soap film. The soap film formed over the wire frame has been broken inside the loop of thread which is distended into the form of a complete circle.*

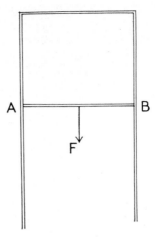

FIG. 147.

surface tension of pure water is about 75 dynes per centimetre at room temperature. That of a soap film is smaller.

In considering the effect the surface tension has on the propagation of waves, it is the pressure which arises when the surface is curved which is important, so we must discuss how this comes about and how big the pressure differences are which can be expected. Two examples will serve to illustrate what is involved. Let us first calculate the difference in pressure between the outside and the inside of a spherical soap bubble.

To get at this, let us first consider a spherical boiler, made up of two hemispheres bolted together, as in the sketch in Fig. 148. The pressure of the steam in the top half will act on the lower half, all over the plane circular opening between the two halves. If the pressure is P pounds per square inch and the radius of the sphere is R inches, the force

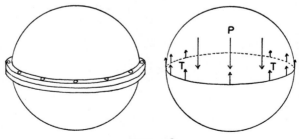

FIG. 148.

exerted by the pressure on the lower half will be $\pi R^2 P$ pounds weight. This force has to be held by the tension of the steel of the boiler, or the bottom would blow off. If this is τ pounds per inch the restraining force will be $2\pi R\tau$, so that

$$\pi R^2 P = 2\pi R\tau$$

or

$$P = \frac{2\tau}{R}$$

If we return now to the soap bubble, a precisely similar calculation can be made. We have to take account of the fact that the soap film has two surfaces, so that the tension per unit length of film is twice the surface tension, $\tau = 2T$ and the excess pressure inside a soap bubble over that outside is

$$P = \frac{4T}{R}$$

If instead of a soap bubble, we considered a water drop, which has only one surface, we would find in a similar way that the formula for the boiler fits the case. The pressure inside a spherical drop caused by the surface tension, is thus

$$P = \frac{2T}{R} \qquad . \qquad . \qquad . \qquad . \qquad 39$$

The pressure varies inversely as the radius and is higher in smaller bubbles than in bigger ones. A small bubble, if connected to a large bubble, will blow the latter up still bigger, itself collapsing in the process.

A sphere is curved in two planes at right angles. The curvature exhibited by waves and ripples is confined, as a rule, to one plane, and the case which ought to be considered for direct application to them is that of a long cylindrical boiler rather than a spherical one.

Consider the equilibrium of one centimetre length of a cylindrical 'boiler' of radius R centimetres (Fig. 149). The force exerted by the pressure P, inside the boiler, on the lower semi-circular portion of length one centimetre, will be

$$P.2R.1$$

This must be balanced by the tension in each side of the section. If this is one centimetre long, the restraining force will be $2T$ ($1T$ being contributed by one edge at A and the second by the other edge at B) so that

$$2P.R = 2T$$

or

$$P = \frac{T}{R} \qquad . \qquad . \qquad . \qquad . \qquad 40$$

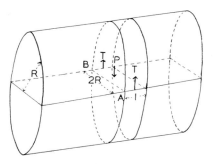

FIG. 149.

In the case of waves, of course, they are not in the form of circular cylinders like the boiler considered above. The curvature of the surface of a long-crested wave, even of the simple form of a sine curve or trochoid, lies in one plane, as in the case of the boiler, but it is not constant from one part of the wave to another. Nevertheless, its curva-

PLATE 57.—*Dissolved substances tend to decrease surface tension. A little alcohol has been dropped into the middle of this layer of coloured water in the white dish. Where the alcohol falls the surface tension is diminished and the stronger tension in distant parts of the water pulls it away from the centre.*

PLATE 58.—*Capillarity. Two glass lantern plates have been stuck together with sealing wax. They are close together on the right-hand side and farther apart (the thickness of a match) on the left. When placed in coloured water it is seen that the water rises highest where the plates are closest together.*

ture at any point may be measured by the circle which fits it closest at that point, and expression 40 gives us the excess pressure we may expect to find immediately underneath the surface when the radius of curvature is R. This is true whether the curvature is positive or negative. We would expect to find an excess pressure under a surface which is convex, like the boiler, but a lowering of pressure under a surface which is concave. How these pressure differences arise may perhaps be better understood if we look at another phenomenon, that of capillarity, which is closely connected with surface tension.

Liquids which wet the surfaces of the bodies with which they are in contact are found to rise in the narrow spaces between, whereas liquids which do not wet the surfaces are depressed to a lower level in such narrow spaces. Plate 58 is a photograph of coloured water between two glass plates, stuck together with sealing wax, forming a wedge. The plates are close together on the right-hand side and wider apart (the thickness of a match stick) on the left. The wedge dips into coloured water in a dish. The water rises above the level in the dish between the plates and stands highest where the plates are closest together. Water also rises in narrow tubes in a similar way. Let us calculate the height to which water will rise in a tube of radius R.

Suppose the water rises to a height h centimetres. The weight of the liquid in a column of this height and radius R is $\pi R^2 \rho g h$, ρ being the

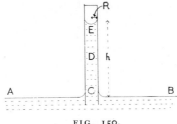

FIG. 150.

density and g the accelerational constant of gravity. This must be balanced by the force of surface tension acting vertically upwards round the circumference of the meniscus of the water in the tube. The length of this circumference is $2\pi R$ so that

$$2\pi RT = \pi R^2 \rho g h$$

giving

$$h = \frac{2T}{R\rho g}$$

By measuring the rise h, in a tube of known radius, we can determine the value of the surface tension T of the liquid. Our interest, however, lies more in the question of the pressures at various points in the liquid. At all points on the flat surface AB (Fig. 150) the pressure will be atmospheric pressure, and this will be true of the point C, at this level inside the tube. As we rise in a liquid the pressure diminishes. The pressure at D and still more at E, just below the surface, must therefore be less than atmospheric pressure. If we made a hole in the side of the tube, water would not flow out. On the contrary, air would flow in. Not much air would, in fact, enter but a new meniscus would form round the hole, as in Fig. 151, but no water would flow out at all.

The point F, just above the surface of the liquid in the tube, will be surrounded by air at atmospheric pressure. There is, therefore, a sudden increase in pressure as we cross the surface of the liquid. This pressure difference is held up by the forces of surface tension. Fig. 152 may help

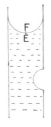

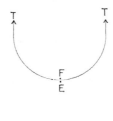

FIG. 151.   FIG. 152.

to make this clear. It is as though someone was pulling upwards on the edges of the surface so that the weight of the liquid in the tube is carried by his effort.

The pressure at E will be $g\rho h$ dynes per square centimetre less than at C where the pressure is atmospheric. If we write this pressure difference P we have

$$P = g\rho h = \frac{2T}{R}$$

just as in Equation 39.

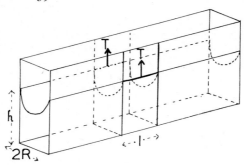

FIG. 153.

If instead of a tube of radius R, we consider parallel plates at a distance $2R$ apart, we would obtain a result applicable to surfaces with a single curvature, as happens in a long wave. The equilibrium of the rectangular prism, dotted in Fig. 153, gives us

$$2T = 1 . 2R . h . \rho g$$

or

$$h\rho g = \frac{T}{R}$$

or

$$h = \frac{T}{R\rho g}$$

both of which expressions will be useful in connection with ripples. Once again $h\rho g$ is the amount by which the pressure just below the surface is less than atmospheric pressure, and this pressure difference is held up by the tension in the surface.

There are many other intriguing phenomena connected with capillarity and surface tension, which it would be possible to discuss, but for information about them the reader must go to books devoted to the subject. The object of this chapter has been to collect together such observations and results about surface tension as are of importance in the propagation of waves, and we are now in a position to return to our main theme.

Q

CHAPTER XIX

Ripples

THE term ripple, in common parlance, is applied to any small wave. It is desirable to restrict the term to waves in the propagation of which surface tension plays the dominant role. If this convention is acceptable, then a ripple is a wave which on water would have to possess a wavelength of less than 1·7 centimetres. The reason for this particular choice of dividing line will become apparent immediately in what follows. Ripples would, therefore, be very small waves indeed. The small waves longer than this, which form on the sea or on lakes and reservoirs, which many would ordinarily refer to as ripples, are in reality nothing more than small gravity waves. They possess the same properties as other gravity waves and surface tension is not an important factor in determining their propagation. We have already seen how small waves on a reservoir possess a group velocity which is only half the wave velocity. This is not true of ripples, properly so called. Indeed a train of ripples possesses a group velocity which is greater than the wave velocity, and, if the wavelength is very small, it is one and a half times as big.

Ripples are present, mixed with waves of other wavelengths, on most occasions when waves are formed. They are most obvious, however, when their presence is not obscured by other waves. They form patterns around objects which move slowly across a water surface, or conversely, when a slow current flows past an obstacle, such as a stone or a fishing line. They are not formed at all, however, unless the relative velocity of the water and the body passing through it is about 23 centimetres per second. In contrast to the gravity waves which spread out behind a ship, ripples occur, in the main, in front of the object producing them. Before attempting to decipher the pattern of ripples produced in such cases, let us inquire a little further into the mechanism whereby surface tension plays a part in the propagation of waves.

The fact of which we have now to take account is that under a curved surface there is a pressure which is greater or less than atmospheric pressure, according to the direction of the curvature. If the radius of curvature at any point is R, then the pressure immediately beneath the surface will be greater or less than atmospheric pressure by an amount $\frac{T}{R}$. This assumes that the curvature is single as with a cylindrical surface and not double as with a sphere. If the curvature occurs in two planes at right angles the pressure difference is double this value. It is greater than atmospheric pressure if the surface is convex to the atmosphere, and less if it is concave. We must first calculate the curvature of our wave surface at various points.

Let us take the case of the simple trochoidal wave, which would include that of the simple harmonic wave of small amplitude, and calculate the curvature at the crests and the troughs.

Let the generating circle (Fig. 154) rolling under the line XY have, as before, a radius k, and let P, the generating point, lie at a distance A from the centre of the circle. Consider what happens as P describes

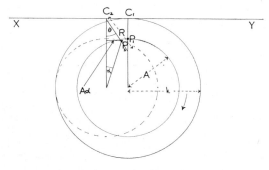

FIG. 154.

the crest of the wave, that is, as it passes the position P_1 in the figure. Since C_1 is the instantaneous centre, the wheel will be turning instantaneously about this point, and P will therefore be travelling at right angles to C_1P_1. Consider the position after the wheel has turned through a very small angle α. The point C moves a distance $k\alpha$ to C_2. The centre of the circle will also move this distance forward. But P will, at the same time, be carried backwards a distance $A\alpha$ because of the rotation of the small circle. The instantaneous centre will have moved to C_2 so that P will now be moving at right angles to the line C_2P_2. In other words C_1P_1 and C_2P_2 are both normals (i.e. they are at right angles) to the waveform which P describes and will intersect at the centre of curvature of this waveform. From simple geometry we have for the angle θ

$$\theta = \frac{A\alpha}{k - A}$$

and also

$$\theta = \frac{k\alpha}{R}$$

where R is the radius of curvature of the waveform.

Hence
$$\frac{A\alpha}{k - A} = \frac{k\alpha}{R}$$

giving
$$R = \frac{k(k - A)}{A}$$

If the amplitude is small we may neglect A when subtracted from k, giving us approximately

$$R = \frac{k^2}{A}$$

But the wavelength
$$\lambda = 2\pi k$$

and therefore
$$R = \frac{\lambda^2}{4\pi^2 . A}$$

The excess pressure under the crest of the wave arising from surface tension will, therefore, be

$$\frac{T}{R} = \frac{4\pi^2 A T}{\lambda^2}$$

Similarly there is a defect of pressure arising from an upward force of surface tension under the troughs, which will be of the same amount if the amplitude of the waves is small. Thus there will be a change in pressure at the surface as we pass from crest to trough of

$$\frac{8\pi^2 A T}{\lambda^2} \quad . \qquad . \qquad . \qquad . \qquad . \qquad 41$$

In our previous calculations, when we neglected surface tension, we assumed that, at the surface, the pressure was always atmospheric. We must now modify that assumption.

Bernoulli's theorem gives us that

$$p + g\rho h + \frac{\rho u^2}{2}$$

is constant along a streamline.

If we take two positions along a streamline denoted by subscripts 1 and 2 we have,

$$p_1 - p_2 + g\rho(h_1 - h_2) + \frac{\rho}{2}(u_1{}^2 - u_2{}^2) = 0$$

Now if the first position is at a crest and the second at a trough we would have

$$p_1 - p_2 = \frac{8\pi^2 A T}{\lambda^2}$$

and $$h_1 - h_2 = 2A$$

so that $$\frac{\rho}{2}(u_2{}^2 - u_1{}^2) = g\rho.2A + \frac{8\pi^2 A T}{\lambda^2}$$

or $$\tfrac{1}{2}(u_2{}^2 - u_1{}^2) = 2A\left(g + \frac{4\pi^2 T}{\rho\lambda^2}\right)$$

In the previous calculations, when we neglected surface tension, we had

$$\tfrac{1}{2}(u_2{}^2 - u_1{}^2) = 2Ag$$

Taking surface tension into account, therefore, is equivalent to changing g to $g + \dfrac{4\pi^2 T}{\rho\lambda^2}$.

Before, we found the velocity of the waves, neglecting surface tension, to be

$$c = \sqrt{\frac{g\lambda}{2\pi}}$$

Taking surface tension into account, we shall have

$$c = \sqrt{\frac{\lambda}{2\pi}\left(g + \frac{4\pi^2 T}{\rho\lambda^2}\right)}$$

$$= \sqrt{\frac{\lambda g}{2\pi} + \frac{2\pi T}{\rho\lambda}} \qquad . \qquad . \qquad . \qquad . \qquad 42$$

We see from this expression that when the wavelength is long the first term under the square root is the important one and the second is small. Long waves are, therefore, controlled by gravity and surface tension has little effect. With short waves, on the other hand, the position is reversed. The first term under the square root is small and the second predominates. Short waves are, therefore, controlled by surface tension and gravity is of small consequence. This is the basis of the distinction between gravity waves and ripples, which we have already given.

The curve C, plotted in Fig. 155, is a graph of Equation 42. It shows that there is a minimum velocity of about 23 centimetres per second, below which no waves are propagated on water. The wavelength corresponding to this minimum velocity of propagation is about 1·73 centimetres. In the case of waves longer than this, which are the gravity waves, properly so called, the velocity increases as the wavelength increases. With the shorter waves, the ripples, on the other hand, the velocity is greater the shorter the wavelength. Near the minimum value the velocity changes only slowly with change in wavelength, so that there is a range of wavelengths all of which are propagated with about the same velocity.

Since waves of wavelength near to 1·7 centimetres all travel with the same velocity, a group is capable of being propagated without change of form. Neither the slightly shorter nor the slightly longer waves will catch up on the others. The group velocity is equal to the wave velocity and the case is comparable to that of gravity waves in shallow water.

With waves longer than the critical length of 1·7 centimetres, the group velocity is less than the wave velocity, because the longer waves overtake the shorter ones, as we have already seen. The opposite is the case for ripples whose wavelength is shorter than the critical length.

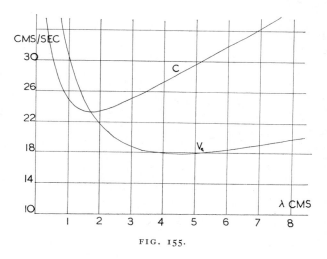

FIG. 155.

Shorter ripples overtake the longer so that the group velocity is greater than the wave velocity. Instead of the point of maximum intensity falling back through the ripples composing a group, and the ripples forming at the rear and dying out as they reach the front of the group, as was the case with gravity waves, ripples form in front of the group and the point of maximum amplitude passes forward over them, so that they die out as the rear of the group reaches them.

The curve labelled V_g in Fig. 155 shows how the group velocity changes with the wavelength of the waves. The curves for c and V_g cross at the minimum of the former, since at that point the wave velocity c and the group velocity V_g are equal. The curve for the group velocity also has a minimum value, however. This occurs at a wavelength of about $4\frac{1}{2}$ centimetres and the group velocity corresponding to

it is 17·8 centimetres per second. Energy cannot, therefore, be transmitted by means of surface waves on water at a smaller velocity than this.

We are now as far as we can get in a simple way towards understanding the pattern of ripples which an object in a stream sets up,
though the situation is far less easy to analyse than was the case of
gravity waves. With the latter those situations commonly met with in
practice usually fell into either the low velocity/deep water class or the
high velocity/shallow water class. The difficult no man's land between
was comparatively uninhabited. The position with regard to ripples is
almost the opposite. The interesting situations appear when the waves
have neither a velocity which is constant for small variations in wavelength nor a well-defined group velocity which is a constant fraction

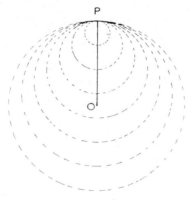

FIG. 156.

of the wave velocity. We may, however, derive some information by
considering what would happen as the velocity of a stream passing a
small object, such as a stone or fishing line, is gradually increased.

Before a speed of 23 centimetres per second is reached no waves can
be slow enough to keep station with the object. Any wavelet or incipient
ripple that is generated will flow away, so that its amplitude cannot be
built up. As soon as the velocity attains the critical value of 23 centimetres per second, this situation changes. With a velocity only slightly
in excess, waves with a wavelength from about 1½ to 2 centimetres are
able to keep pace and their group velocity is also about the same as that
of the stream. Wavelets of these wavelengths generated at all points
previously passed through by the object (or carried past it by the
stream) will reinforce at the object itself. The situation is depicted in
Fig. 156. It is only in the directly forward direction that the waves are
able to keep station with the object and the ripple pattern, therefore,

takes the form of a short ripple or two at right angles to the path. The position is a little more complicated than this because water will be slowed up in front of the object and thus the stream can reach the critical velocity at points distant from the object while the water near it is still travelling more slowly. The ripple will, therefore, form in front of the object at a place before the stream has been retarded.

The photograph of which Plate 59 is a reproduction, is of the pattern of ripples set up by a small object in a stream of water, flowing with a velocity only slightly exceeding the critical value at which ripples

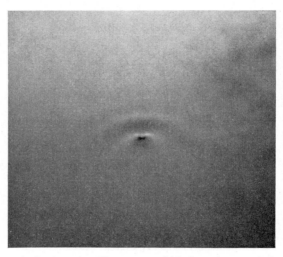

PLATE 59.—*Ripples in water. The stream, which flows downwards in the picture, is flowing just fast enough for the small object to cause ripples. They form in front of the object, on the upstream side.*

form. The stream flows from top to bottom in the photograph and the ripples are almost entirely upstream of the object causing them, as we have been led to expect from our considerations of their method of generation.

As the speed of the stream is increased, there will still be a group of waves with wavelengths near to 1·7 centimetres, all of which are propagated with the same velocity. They will give rise to a wake with the result that two arms are formed, like the arms in a wake of gravity waves, and these bend backwards as the speed of the stream increases, as in Figs. 157 and 158. The position is very similar to the one we studied in connection with gravity waves in shallow water.

When the velocity of the stream is considerably in excess of 23

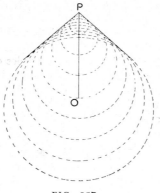

FIG. 157.

centimetres per second, the fact that the group velocity of ripples is greater than the wave velocity begins to affect the pattern. By the time the wavefront generated by the object when at O (Fig. 159) has spread to the circumference of the circle of radius OT, the groups will have been propagated farther out, and lie on the circumference of the circle of radius OT'. By an argument similar to that used in the case of wakes formed by gravity waves, the wake will consist of two arms radiating from P. These arms will comprise ripples whose fronts are parallel to PT. They are thus inclined to the line of the wake, as was the case with the gravity waves, but in the opposite direction. The tendency for this to happen is clearly shown in the photograph in Plate 63, with the stream of the highest speed. Because of the absence of any simple relation between the wave velocity and group velocity, such as obtained

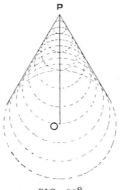

FIG. 158.

for gravity waves on deep water, however, it is a difficult matter to calculate the exact angle.

There is one other factor on which it is possible to comment. It is that since the stream is slowed up by the object and will be travelling faster a little away from it than close to, ripples of smaller wavelength will be found keeping station with the object a little way ahead.

To discuss the exact patterns of ripples over the entire surface in the neighbourhood of an object moving relatively to the water, would require elaborate mathematics. In this book we must content ourselves with these few theoretical observations. Ripples, however, are not difficult to study practically. A stream of water may be made to flow

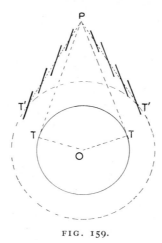

FIG. 159.

past a small object, and the ripple pattern set up may be observed directly, or projected on to a screen as shadows cast by a motor car lamp mounted below. Some photographs taken in this way, using a very simple trough made from a sheet of glass with sides fastened to it with adhesive tape, are reproduced in Plates 60, 61, 62 and 63. Those features to be expected on the theoretical grounds the discussion of which forms the bulk of this chapter, may be compared with observations from these records. The general theoretical picture appears substantially to be correct.

The ripples which figure in the photographs are such as would be set up by a fishing line stationary in a stream of water. Actually they are formed by a piece of wire, of similar diameter to a fishing line, and the photographs were obtained by means of water flowing in the simple trough mentioned in the previous paragraph. The ripples of Plate 60

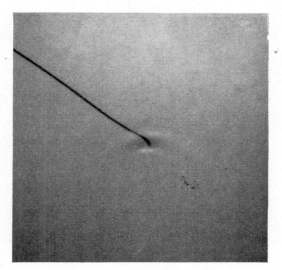

PLATE 60.—*Ripples in water. Ripples just being formed by a 'fishing line' in very slowly running water. The stream runs from top to bottom in the picture and the ripples form on the upstream side of the line. They take the form of small arcs of circles.*

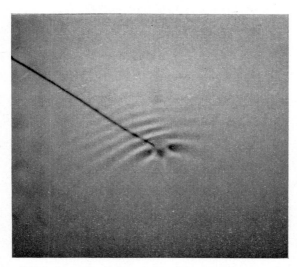

PLATE 61.—*Ripples in water. As the velocity of the stream increases the wavelength of the ripples diminishes and the arcs spread out laterally.*

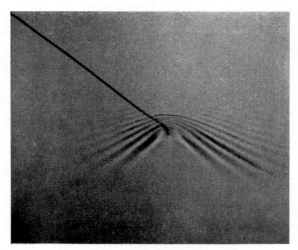

PLATE 62.—*Ripples in water. As the velocity of the stream increases still further a wake, formed of two arms, starts to form. In the arms, where the ripples travel obliquely, the wavelength is longer than directly ahead where they have to travel faster to maintain station with the line.*

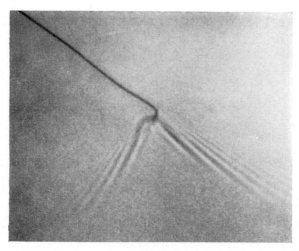

PLATE 63.—*Ripples in water. Here the speed of the water is greater still. Two arms are formed which bend backwards more than previously. The arms are formed of wavelets which cross them at an angle which is in the opposite direction to that which occurs in ships' wakes of longer wavelength.*

238

were formed when the velocity of the water was only slightly in excess of 23 centimetres per second, and they are very similar to those of Plate 59. In Plate 61 the velocity of the stream is somewhat greater. The pattern remains substantially the same though it is more extensive. The ripples remain predominantly in front of the line.

In Plate 62 the velocity of the stream has been further increased and three features are displayed in the photograph, which deserve comment. First there is the obvious bending back of the arms of the wake in accordance with our previous considerations. Secondly, the wavelength of the ripples has diminished considerably (the photographs are on the same scale). To maintain station in the more rapid stream the ripples must be propagated at a higher speed and thus possess a shorter wavelength. The third feature which this photograph shows very clearly is the change in wavelength of the ripples with their direction of propagation. When the ripples travel obliquely to the stream, they need only possess a lower velocity of propagation to maintain station with the fishing line, than is necessary when they are propagated directly against the stream. Ripples facing straight up stream, therefore, possess a shorter wavelength than those facing obliquely to the stream. Since, near the critical speed, the velocity of the ripples changes only slowly with wavelength, there is a very considerable difference between the wavelengths of the ripples facing up stream and those travelling obliquely. The wavelengths in this photograph are in the ratio of three to one approximately.

In Plate 63 there has been a further increase in the speed of the stream. There is a consequent further folding back of the arms of the wake, but the more interesting feature to be seen in this photograph is that it approximates very closely to Fig. 159. The wake is composed of two arms with the component waves crossing it at an angle. The waves, moreover, cross the line of the arms inclined in the opposite direction to that in which gravity waves cross the arms in a ship's wake. This is as we would expect from the fact that with ripples the group velocity exceeds the wave velocity.

CHAPTER XX

Reflections in Rippled Water

REFLECTIONS in water are modified by the rippling of the surface either by small gravity waves or by ripples, properly so called, and the patterns to which this gives rise can add a great deal of interest to walks by lake or stream. They provide many opportunities for those who like observing nature in the field to exercise their acuity. No recondite knowledge is required and much enjoyment is to be obtained in the recording of observations either by paint brush or camera. A little thought beforehand can open the eyes about what to look out for, and it is the purpose of this chapter to unlock this door for those who have not thought much about the matter before.

When water is still it reflects like a mirror and images are produced by its surface as in a looking glass. These images, of course, appear to lie below the surface, and, as with a mirror, they are situated as far below the surface as the objects which are reflected are above. Nevertheless, what the eye sees reflected in the water is not a mere replica of what it sees directly. Many of the objects which can be seen directly are not visible in the reflection, and conversely, though quite so commonly, the images of objects which cannot be seen directly may be observed in the water. This is caused by a shift in the viewpoint. Those objects are visible in the reflections which could be seen were the eye to be placed in a position as much below the surface of the water as it stands at present above it. They are, of course, seen inverted. Low objects on the banks, such as cattle in the water meadows bordering a river, are unlikely to be present in the reflections. High objects which tower above the banks, however, have their tops reflected in the stream. The tops of distant mountains may be clearly visible while the intermediate distances are masked by the banks or other comparatively low objects, close to.

There is also a somewhat less obvious change in colour. Bright colours, strongly illuminated, are reflected with little alteration, but darker colours are affected by the colour of the water. The water, if illuminated, possesses a colour of its own. This, as a rule, is not very intense and is easily masked by bright reflections. It becomes apparent, however, in the reflections of dark surfaces. It is to be seen whether the surface of the water is still or moderately rippled. For example, the reflections of the buildings on the Grand Canal in Venice, in Plates XVIII and XIX, show up in their own colours, when these are bright, but the reflections of the darker buildings are in the green colour of the water of the canal. A very similar thing happens in the atmosphere. The air itself possesses a very weak blue colour. It can be seen only when it is possible to look through long lengths of air, as when we look up at the sky. When we look at very distant objects we see their bright surfaces in very nearly their proper colour, the colour of the light scattered by the air being insufficient to modify it appreciably. In the darker places, however, we are able to detect the colour of the atmosphere and this causes them to appear bluish.

The masking of faint light by reflections is familiar enough when we try to see into the water itself. In positions where the sky is reflected in the surface it is more often than not impossible to see the bottom at all. To observe the fish in the river we have to look in places where some dark object, such as the trunk of a tree, is reflected. Rippling of the surface makes this more difficult. Not only does it distort the outline of the things in the water through refraction, but it also introduces reflections of the sky in the inclined surfaces of the ripples, in places where it might otherwise be possible to see into the water. There is, also, another factor which comes into play in this connection. The proportion of the light which falls on the surface of water or other transparent material, which is reflected, increases as its direction becomes more nearly parallel to the surface. At glancing angles the proportion reflected may be very high, whereas when the light falls more nearly at right angles to the surface, much more of it is transmitted into the water and less is reflected. We see things in the water most clearly, therefore, when we are able to look as nearly straight down into it as possible. The amount of light reflected from the sky and other places above the water is then at its least and masks least what we want to see, and also the proportion of the light from the bottom or from the objects in the water which we want to look at, which is able to emerge from the surface, is greatest. The bottom of a lake is rarely visible for more than a few yards from the shore even when the water is still and there is a dark background like a mountain behind. The bottom, however, may have a visible effect even when it cannot be seen itself directly at all. One which reflects a great deal of light will enhance the body colour of the water and may make itself felt in a subtle way by enhancing the colour of the water in the dark reflections.

When the surface of the water is disturbed we see reflections from the inclined surfaces of the ripples. At a little distance away the far sides of the ripples are screened from us and only the near surfaces are visible. These reflect the sky. Areas of rippled water, therefore, show up as lines of light colour—the colour of the sky—across the images of the distant objects reflected in the surface. The effect of perspective is to cause these lines to run very nearly horizontally across a photograph, as can be seen from Figs. 160a and b. The ellipse shows the appearance of a distant circle viewed at an angle of 15°. The straight lines in Fig. 160a give the position of equally spaced radial lines drawn from the centre of the circle. In Fig. 160b we see the position of these lines projected on to the plane of the paper. The positions are, of course, the same in both cases, as can be demonstrated by tracing the ellipse on a piece of plain paper, cutting it out and superimposing the paper on Fig. 160b, so that the lines are seen through the hole.

However, it is exceptional for distant objects in a landscape to be seen at an angle as large as 15° with the horizontal. The elevation of the sun

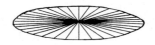

FIG. 160a.

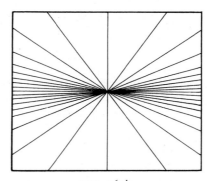

FIG. 160b.

in Colour Plate XV, for example, amounts only to 5°, and even this angle would be large for most landscapes. Fig. 161 shows a similar diagram to that in Fig. 160 but drawn from an angle of 5° instead of 15°. This is still a large angle. In scenes such as that photographed in Plate XVI the angle at which the distant water surface is viewed would be a good deal less than 1°. The apparent concentration of lines drawn on the surface into the direction at right angles to the line of sight, which in the case of a water surface would have to lie horizontally, is obvious. The higher we are, ourselves, above the surface, the more of the sky do we see reflected in the water, so that lakes and rivers seen from above look like molten lead and are devoid of the reflections of neighbouring objects.

Clear water shows no shadows cast upon it by objects in a position to do so, though foam does, if it is present. The only effect which light incident upon water can have, if it is not reflected to the eye, is to enhance the body colour of the water. This, as we have seen, affects the colour of the reflections of dark objects, so that what is to be expected in a shadow cast upon clear water would be that the presence of the body colour of the water in the reflections might be less marked. It is not at all an easy effect to discern, especially if the illumination is not brilliant. Muddy water, on the other hand, shows shadows cast upon itself, and also its effect upon the colour of dark reflections is more marked, since it possesses a marked colour of its own.

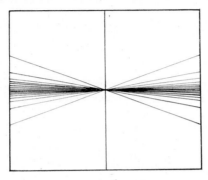

FIG. 161.

Perhaps the most striking fact about reflections in rippled water is the long drawing out of the vertical lines. This is seen most clearly in the reflection of bright objects such as the lights on ships or the shore, or of the sun and the moon. The long lanes of light in these cases are a familiar sight. At the same time horizontal lines, even if possessing considerable brilliance, are smudged out and often practically invisible in the reflections. This drawing out of reflections in the direction of the observer applies, of course, to everything. It becomes most noticeable in the case of bright reflections, the colour of the water itself predominating elsewhere. Reflections of clouds are often only to be seen in the case of the brightest parts, those of the darker portions being very difficult to detect. This can be seen, for example, in the photograph of Colour Plate XX, very well.

Since we might expect the direction of the ripples on water to take one direction as much as any other, whence comes this apparent preference for the vertical direction in the elongation of reflections? It is of interest to investigate this question in a little more detail. Let us

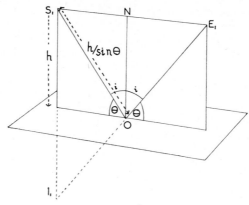

FIG. 162.

examine the case of the reflection of the sun or the moon in rippled water.

Consider the reflection of a ray of sunlight S_1O which is reflected in a still horizontal surface at O (Fig. 162). After reflection the ray traces out the path OE_1, making the same angle θ with the water surface as did the incident ray S_1O, so that an eye placed to receive it at E_1 will see the image of the sun in the direction OI_1. In this case the initial ray S_1O and the reflected ray OE_1 will lie in a vertical plane, and ON, the vertical line through O (the point where the ray is reflected), also lies in this plane.

Let us now consider what happens when the surface at O is tilted at a small angle ε, so that the line at right angles to it, which was initially vertical and lay along O_1N (Fig. 163), will also turn through

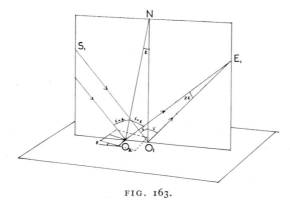

FIG. 163.

the same angle ε. First let us take the case when the line at right angles to the surface remains in the vertical plane containing S_1O_1 and O_1E_1, so that the surface is tilted towards, or away from, the observer. Tilt in this direction will draw out the reflection towards, or away, from the observer also.

In Fig. 163 is drawn a small portion of the tilted surface at O_2. When a reflector is turned through an angle ε, the reflected ray is turned through twice that angle, as may be verified from Fig. 163. If ε is the largest inclination of the surface of the ripples, the angle subtended at the eye by that half of the lane of glitter which lies above the perfect image in a still surface, is thus 2ε. There will be a similar extension of the image towards the observer, so that the total angle in the vertical plane through sun and observer is 4ε.

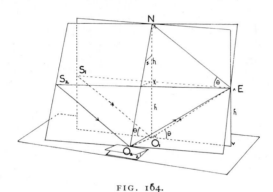

FIG. 164.

Now let us inquire into the lateral spread of the image, in a direction at right angles to this. To discuss this we refer to Fig. 164. Let h be the height of the eye above the water surface. When the surface is tilted a new ray S_2O_2 will be reflected to the eye still situated at E. S_2O_2, coming from the distant sun, will be parallel to the first ray S_1O_1. E, O_2 and S_2 will define a new plane. When ε is small it will be seen from the figure that

$$O_1O_2 = 2h\varepsilon$$

Thus the semi-lateral angle of the image will be

$$\frac{O_1O_2}{O_1E} = \frac{O_1O_2}{h} \sin\theta = \frac{2h\varepsilon \sin\theta}{h} = 2\varepsilon \sin\theta$$

The total angle subtended by the image laterally will thus be $4\varepsilon \sin\theta$. The ratio of the lateral to the longitudinal angles subtended by the image is equal to $\sin\theta$. Here θ is the angle of elevation of the sun. For the sun at midday in the summer θ will be of the order of 60° for a place in latitude $53\frac{1}{2}$° N. The ratio of the length to the breadth of the area of glitter on a water surface caused by the sun would be expected to be about 1·55. In the winter at midday the elevation of the sun would be about 13° and the ratio 4·45. When the sun is low in the sky, the ratio can, of course, be greater still. When it is only some 5° above the horizon, as in Plate XV, the path formed by the reflection can extend from the horizon to close to the observer. It does not reach the horizon in Plate XV because of the shadow cast by the bank of clouds beneath the sun in the picture; otherwise it would do so.

This drawing out of reflections in the direction from the observer to the object, explains how it is that vertical lines tend to be preserved in the images whereas horizontal lines are lost, a fact we have already remarked upon. Objects of limited dimension only become visible in reflections in disturbed water if they are bright enough for their image to be seen when elongated in this way by the ripples.

The theory of this effect which has just been given explains why the phenomenon occurs. The ratio of length to breadth of the glitter path will only accord with observation if the disturbance of the surface is haphazard and therefore likely to be as great in one direction as another. This will not often be the case, since ripples are normally caused by wind and tend to travel in a definite direction. They never, however, take the form of indefinitely long corrugations, so that there is always some tilt in the direction of the observer. The angle of elevation at which most reflections are observed is such that the effect of tilt towards the observer outweighs any preponderance there may be in other directions.

These long paths of glittering water always point directly towards the observer wherever he may be. They move round as the observer moves, so that this is always the case. Just as the rainbow seen by one observer is different from that seen by another and in a different part of the sky, so each observer sees his own glitter path which is special to him. It is not possible to see a path directed towards any other observer.

Index

Accelerometers 117
Admiralty Navigation Manual 140
Admiralty Swell Forecasting Section
    112, 121
Admiralty Weather Manual, Sea Dis-
    turbance Table 140
Adverse current, Lord Rayleigh's
    method of 51, 67, 130
Aegir on River Trent 35, 38
Age of tide 15
Alde, River 88
Aldeburgh 88
Amphidromic point 31
Ardrossan and Glasgow Canal 81
Avonmouth 37

Bagnold 84
Banks, height of bore near 55
Barker and Ursell 112, 123
Basins, tides in circular 30
Batsham, port of 3
Bay of Fundy, tide in 27, 29, 42
Beats in sound waves 121, 189
Beaufort Scale of wind force 139
Beechey, Captain 34
Bernoulli, Daniel 87
Bernoulli's theorem 101–11, 130
Bertelli, Father Timoteo 148
Blue of distant shadows 241
Boat rowed in waves 83
Boiler, pressure inside cylindrical 223
    pressure inside spherical 222
Bores, experimental demonstration of
        velocity 45
    initiation of 57
    negative 69, 79
    theory of 50, 64
Breakers, plunging and spilling 89
Breaking of waves, in deep water
    142, 163
    in shallow water 74, 77, 89
Breakwaters 91
Bristol Channel 29
Buchau, sailing vessel 105
Buys Ballot's law 29

Cambridge wave recorder 114

Camphor, movement on water 220
Capillarity 225
Cartwright and Rydill 127
Caudebec-en-Caux 39, 40, 56
Chesil Bank 88
Chien Tang Kiang, River 38, 42, 44,
    63, 64
Circular basins, tides in 30
Clapotis 94, 164, 168
Coast erosion 85
Conrad, Joseph 112
Cornish, Dr Vaughan 34, 112, 138,
    140, 141
Cotidal lines, for English Channel 24
    for Irish Sea 25
    for North Sea 32
Curvature of trochoidal waves 229
Cycle of Saros 19
Cycloidal waves 156

Darbyshire 149
Deacon, on height of waves 138
    on microseisms 149
Dead water 212
Deben, River 88
Declination of sun and moon 3, 17
Denmark 31
Diffraction of waves 186 et seq.
Discovery II 120, 127
Distant objects, colour of 241
Doppler shift in frequency 125
Double high water 3
Drops, shape of liquid 218

Eddies 169 et seq.
    behind symmetrical windmill 181
    effect in aiding transport of solids
        88
    from aerofoil 175
    in cigarette smoke 175
    in lee of waves 145
    in pipes 174, 175
Ekman 212
Energy of waves 90
English Channel, tides in 24–31
Epney 36
Equilibrium tide 2 et seq.

Equinoctial tides   18
Erosion   85
Estuary, model of Severn   34
   tides in   33

Falkland Islands, waves arising near
   123, 125
Fetch   140
Floating a needle on water   218
Floodgates, flow of water under   110
Floods, of 1571   98
   of 1763 and 1779   100
Flow over a weir   109
Fly-boat, Scottish   82
Forth and Clyde Canal   82
Fourier   121
Framilode   36
Frampton Sands   35, 63
French coast, high tides on   30
Froude's law   183, 211
Fundy, Bay of   27, 29, 42

Gainsborough   38
Galileo   2
Generation of waves   138 et seq.
Gerstner   157
Gibson, A. H.   34
Glasgow and Ardrossan Canal   81
Gloucester   36, 54
Gravitation, Law of   6
Gravity waves, in deep water   128
   in shallow water   67
Ground swell   123
Group velocity   123, 193
Groups of waves   121
Gunness   38
Gutenberg   148

Haining   38, 44, 64
Hang Chau   44, 63
Hanging of perigee   15
Hanoi   3
Heave of ships   126
Height of tide, at sea   30
   at Sharpness   35
Height of waves   112, 138
Holinshed   98
Holland   31, 98
Hooke, Robert   186
Houston, William   81
Hugo, Victor   39
Huyghens' Construction   78

Imbo   149
Interference of waves   93, 165, 186
   et seq.
Irish Sea, tides in   25

Jeffreys' sheltering theory   145

Kelvin, Lord   20, 81, 82, 202
Kent, River   39, 63
Kepler   2
Klotz   148

La Bouille   40
Lagging of tide   3, 16
Laska   148
Lee shores   141
Le Havre   39
Long Island Sound, tides in   27, 29
Longuet-Higgins   84, 152
Lunar month   19
Lynch, Father   154

Magellan, Straits of   27, 29
Magnus effect   104, 182
Maisemore   36
Mascaret   39, 40, 42, 56
Meanders of rivers   88
Mersey, River   39
Metonic cycle   20
Microseisms   148 et seq.
Miles' theory of wave generation   147
Mill on the Floss   38
Mill-race   110
Minsterworth   36
Moon   2 et seq.
Moon's declination   17
   distance   5
   motion   15
   motion, nodes of   19
Moore, Usborne   38, 43, 44, 63, 64

Narrowing of rivers, effect on surface
   level   65
National Institute of Oceanography
   114, 117, 122, 149
Neap tides   3, 15
Needle floating on water   218
Negative bore   69, 79
New Brunswick   42
Newnham   37, 54
Newton and the tides   2, 3, 17

Nodes, of interfering waves 94
  of moon's motion 19
  tidal 27
Noose Sands 35, 63
North Sea, Cotidal lines for 32
Norway, tidal range and amphidromic
  point near 31

Orwell, River 88
Oscillations of sea 26, 98

Parrett, River 39, 63
Pattern, of ripples near obstacle 233
  et seq.
  of waves set up by ships 201
  et seq.
Perigee springs 15
Periods, of deep water waves 134
  of seas and gulfs 29
Perranporth wave-recording station
  123
Perspective, effect on reflections 242
Petitcodiac, River 42
Phillips' theory of wave generation
  146
Piezo-electric wave recorder 115
Pitching of ships at sea 126
Plunging breakers 89
Priming of tide 3, 16
Pull of golf drive 103

Quarter diurnal tide 21
Quarters of the moon 15

Ramirez 149
Rayleigh, Lord 51, 67, 72, 196
Recording of waves 112
Redgauntlet 38
Reflection, of sea waves at break-
  waters 91, 92
  of sun 244
Reflections in rippled water 240
  et seq.
Refraction of sea waves 95
Resonance of tides 26
Resonant frequencies for tides 26
Resonant lengths of seas and gulfs 28
Reynolds, Osborne 174, 182, 184,
  211
Rip current 85, 96
Ripples 228 et seq.
  pattern of near obstacle 233

River meanders 88
Rolling of ships at sea 126
Rouen 39, 42, 56
Rowing boat in waves 83
Russell, John Scott 81
Rydill and Cartwright 127

Saint Michel 42
Saros, cycle of 19
Scott, Sir Walter 38
Scottish Fly-boat transport 82
Scripps Institution 141
Sea walls 91, 92
'Second shove' 38
Seine, River 39, 42, 56
Semi-diurnal tide 10, 21
Severn, bore 34, 55, 64
  Bridge 35, 36
  estuary 36
  estuary, model of 34
  River 34, 36, 63
Shakespeare micrometer 114
Shape of liquid drops 218
Ship-borne wave recorder 119
Ships' wakes, in deep water 201
  in shallow water 212
Short-crested waves 126
Slice of golf drive 103
Sluice, flow of water under 110
Smoke rings 178
Soap films 220
Solway Firth 38, 42
Speed numbers of tides 23
Spilling breakers 89
Spin, effect of on projectiles 103
Spring tides 3, 15, 35
Springs, perigee 15
Stevenson, Thomas 140
Stockwith 38
Stokes 84, 121
Stonebench 36
Suffolk coast 31
Superposition, principle of 186
Surface current 84, 135, 137
Surface level, variation in 59
Surface tension 215 et seq.
Surges 98
Swell, Admiralty Forecasting Section
  112, 121
  ground 123

Tait, Professor 103

Tank, wave 44
Tidal bores 33 et seq.
  theory of 50 et seq.
Tidal components 22
Tidal currents 22, 29
Tidal waves 97, 98
Tides 2 et seq.
  age of 15
  constituents 22
  effectiveness of sun and moon 13
  equilibrium 2 et seq.
  equinoctial 18
  in circular seas 30
  in estuaries 33
  in shallow water 21
  lag of 3, 16
  neap 15, 35
  nodes of 27
  perigee springs 15
  predicting machine 20
  priming of 3, 16
  quarter diurnal 21
  raising force 3 et seq.
  semi-diurnal 10, 21
  speed number of 23
  spring 3, 15, 35
  variation with the distance of the
    sun and moon 11, 12, 13
  winter and summer 16
Torricelli's theorem 111
Transport of material by waves 70,
  77, 83, 88
Trent, aegir on 35, 38
  River 34, 56
Trochoidal waves 77, 155 et seq.
  curvature of surface of 229
Trommsdorf 149
Tucker, wave recorder 117, 119

Undertow 84
Ursell and Barker 112, 123
U.S. Military Sea Transport Service
  127

Vacquier, Charles 39

Velocity of propagation, of harmonic
  waves in deep water 122, 132,
  133, 134
  of negative bore 69, 79
  of tidal bore 37, 38, 53
  of trochoidal waves in deep water
    157–62
  of waves in shallow water 71
Villequier 39
Vortices 179
Vortex ring 178

Wakes, of ships in deep water 201
  of ships in shallow water 212
Waves, breaking of in shallow water
  74, 77, 89
  diffraction of 186 et seq.
  effect on rowing boat 83
  energy of 90
  generation of 138 et seq.
  groups 121
  heights of 112, 138
  in deep water, theory of 128 et seq.
  in shallow water, experimental
    demonstration of velocity of 46
  in shallow water, theory of 67 et
    seq.
  interference of 93, 165, 186 et seq.
  recorders for 112 et seq.
  reflection of 92
  refraction of 95
  solitary 69
  spectra of 121 et seq.
  transport of material by 70, 77, 83,
    88
  velocity of propagation of in deep
    water 132, 133, 134
  velocity of propagation of in shallow
    water 71
Wave tank 44
Wave velocity and group velocity
  123
Wiechert 148

Yawing of ships 126